Arranged for portable keyboards *by Kenneth Baker.*

THE COMPL
KEYBOARD PLAYER
ANTHOLOGY

CW00741328

Wise Publications
London/New York/Paris/Sydney

Exclusive Distributors:
Music Sales Limited
14/15 Berners Street, London W1T 3LJ, England.
Music Sales Pty, Limited
20 Resolution Drive, Caringbah, NSW 2229, Australia.

This book © Copyright 1992 by Wise Publications
Order No.AM89550
ISBN 0-7119-3042-2

Book design by Pearce Marchbank Studio
Compiled by Peter Evans
Music arranged by Kenneth Baker

Printed in the United Kingdom by
Caligraving Limited, Thetford, Norfolk.

NORWEGIAN WOOD

Words & Music by John Lennon & Paul McCartney

Suggested registration: guitar
Rhythm: waltz
Tempo: fast (♩ = 176)

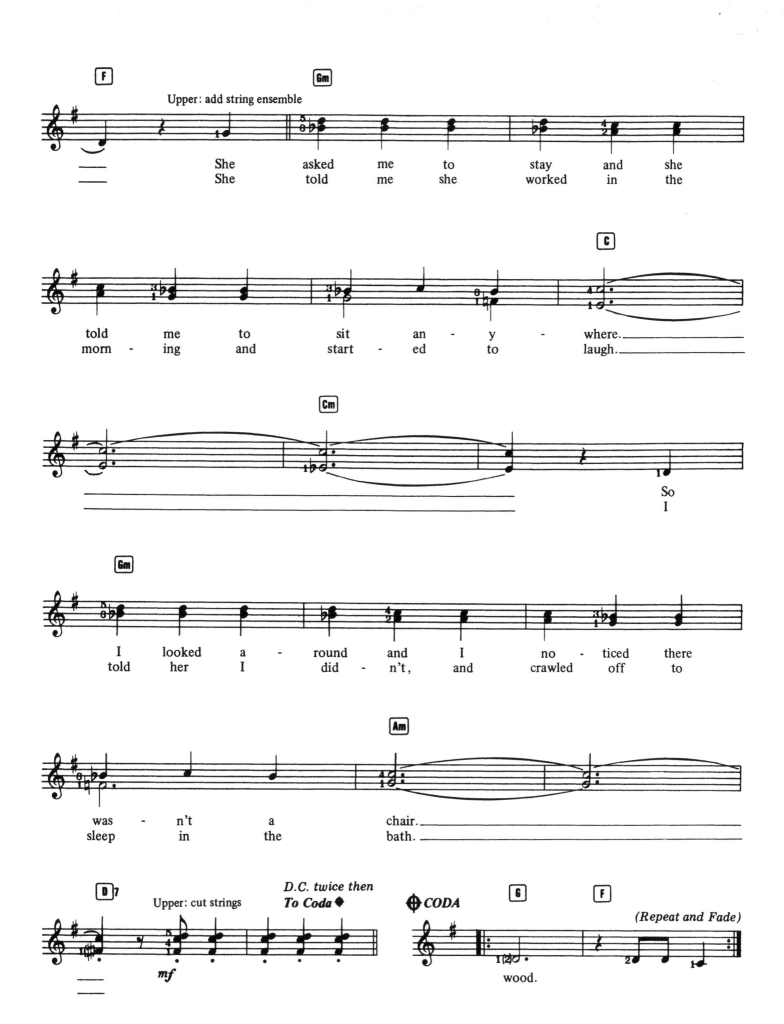

BALLADE POUR ADELINE

Composed by Paul de Senneville

Suggested registration: piano, with full sustain
Arpeggio, if available
Rhythm: beguine (or bossa nova)
Tempo: medium (♩ = 120)

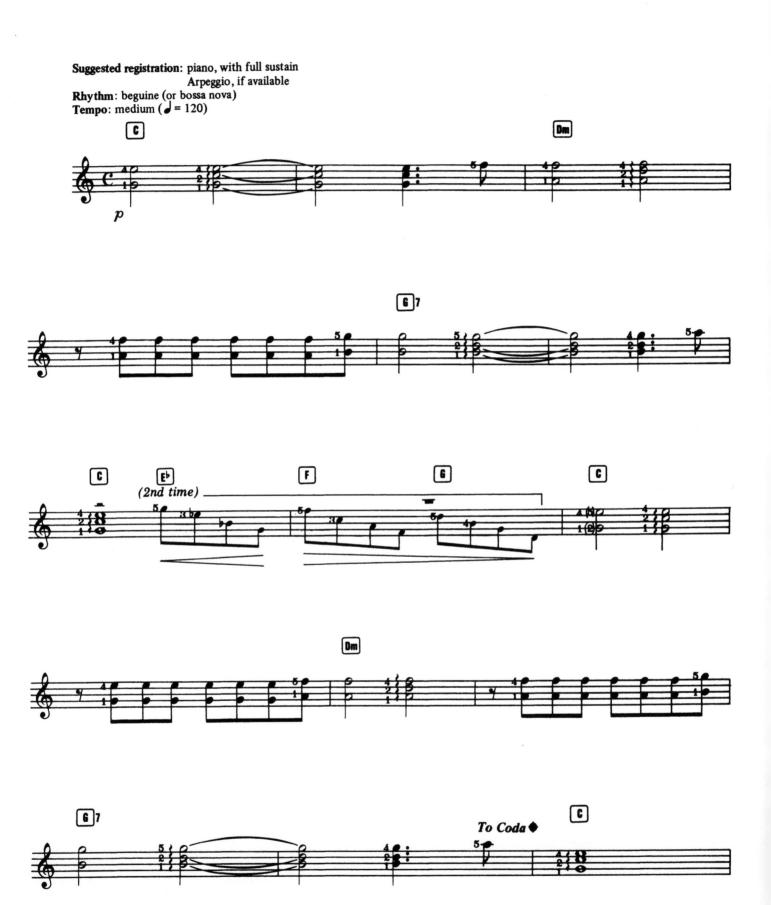

ON GOLDEN POND (THEME FROM)

Composed by Dave Grusin

Suggested registration: Piano,
with full sustain + Chorus

Rhythm : Off (play ad lib)

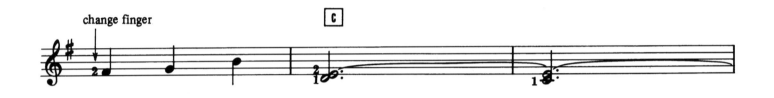

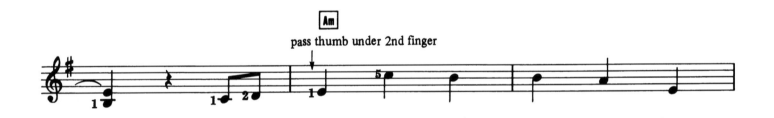

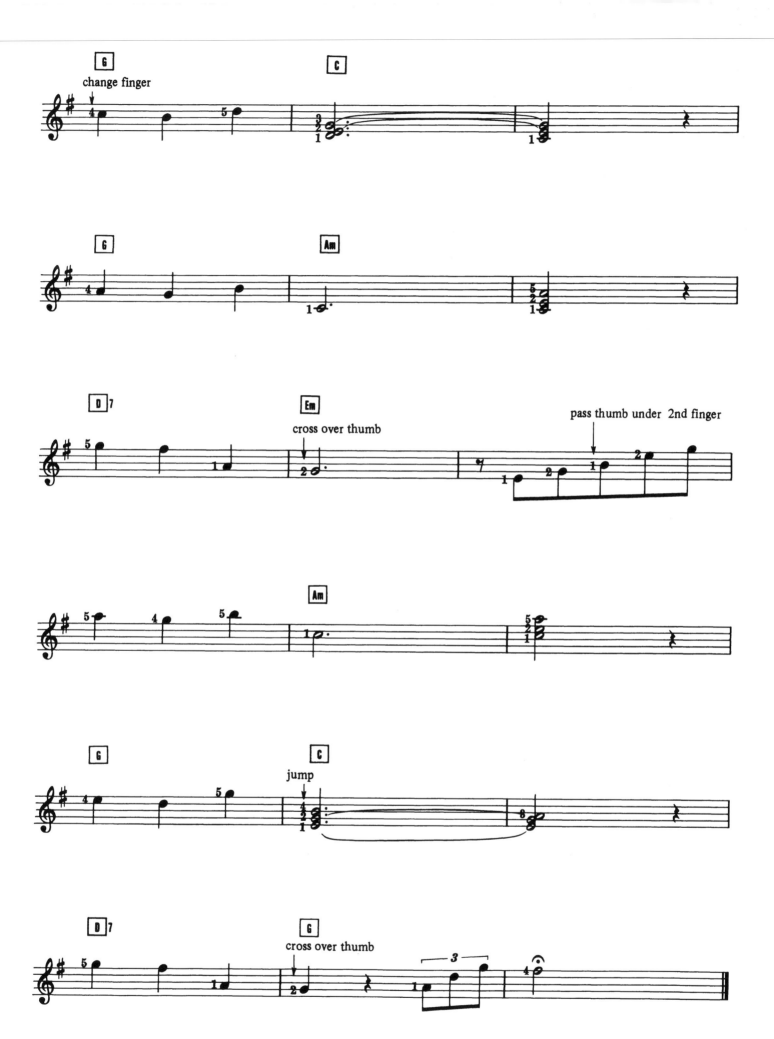

WHAT I DID FOR LOVE

Words by Edward Kleban. Music by Marvin Hamlisch

Suggested registration: String ensemble

Rhythm : Bossa nova
Tempo : medium ($\downarrow$ =96)
Synchro-start, if available

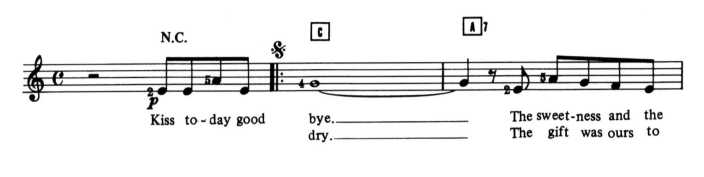

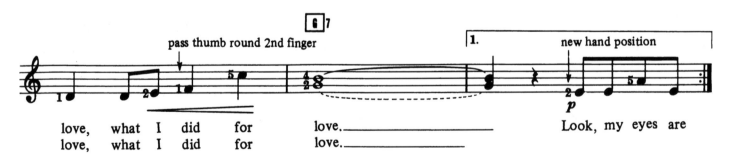

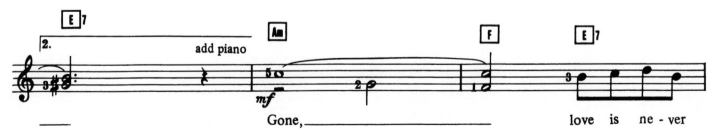

gone._____ As we trav-el on,_____

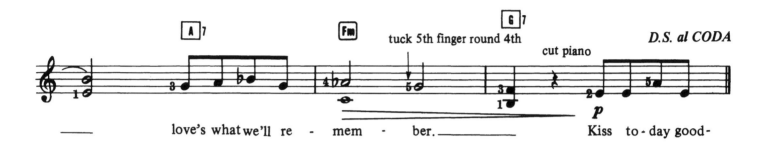

____ love's what we'll re - mem - ber._____ Kiss to-day good-

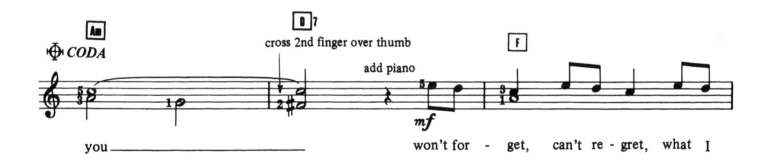

you_____ won't for - get, can't re - gret, what I

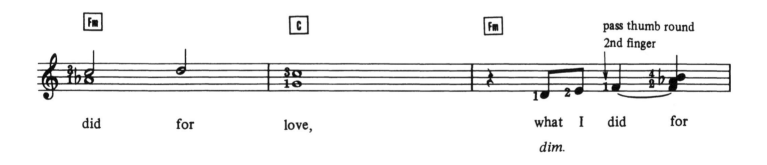

did for love, what I did for

love. What I did for love._____

AGAINST ALL ODDS
(TAKE A LOOK AT ME NOW)

Words & Music by Phil Collins

Suggested registration: Electric Piano
(with sustain) + Chorale

Rhythm : Rock
Tempo : Slow 2 (♩=66)

How can I just let - you walk a - way, just let you
How can you just walk - a - way from me, when all I can

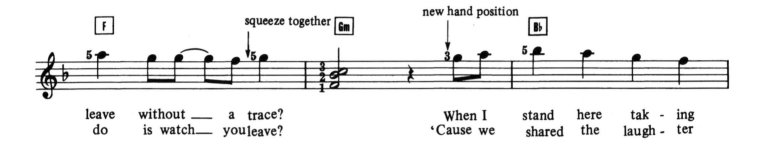

leave without ___ a trace? When I stand here tak - ing
do is watch ___ you leave? 'Cause we shared the laugh - ter

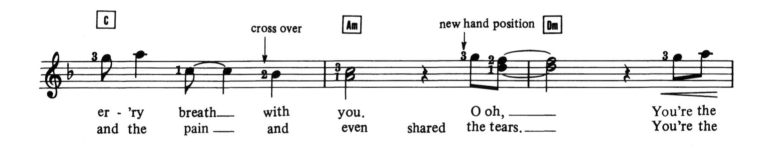

er - 'ry breath ___ with you. O oh, ___ You're the
and the pain ___ and even shared the tears. ___ You're the

on - ly one who real - ly knew me at all. ___
on - ly one who real - ly knew me at all. ___

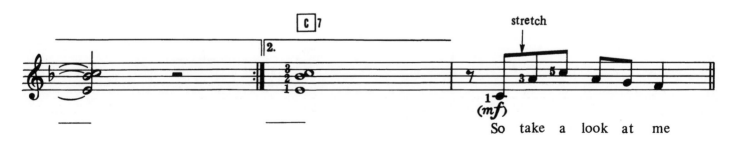

So take a look at me

now. ___ Well, there's just an emp - ty space, _____

and there's noth -ing left here to - re - mind - me_____ just the

mem - 'ry of your face._ Well, take a look at me now._____

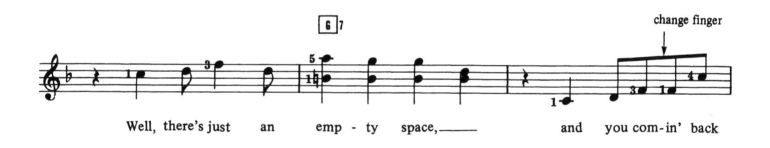

Well, there's just an emp - ty space,_____ and you com-in' back

___ to me is a - gainst___ the odds,___and that's what I've got to face___

___ Take a look at me now. _____

EASTENDERS

Composed by Leslie Osborne & Simon May

Suggested registration: Harpsichord
+ Synthe (with sustain)

Rhythm : Rock
Tempo : medium (♩=96)

(Fine)

cross 2nd finger over thumb

D.C. al Fine

HEY JUDE

Words & Music by John Lennon & Paul McCartney

Suggested registration: guitar
Rhythm: rock
Tempo: medium (♩ = 92)
Synchro-start, if available

A FOGGY DAY

Music by George Gershwin

Suggested registration: accordion & chorus
Rhythm: swing
Tempo: quite fast (♩ = 152)

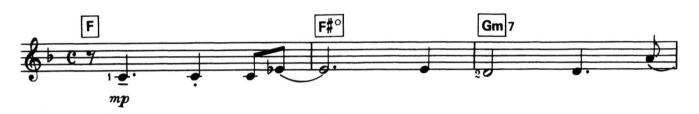

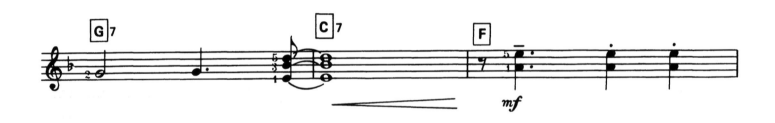

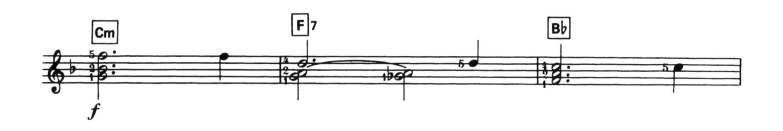

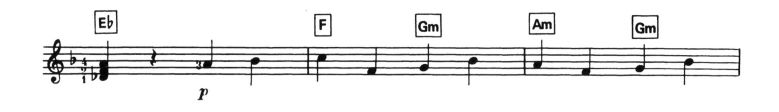

19

SATIN DOLL

Words by Johnny Mercer. Music by Duke Ellington & Billy Strayhorn

Suggested registration: vibes (with sustain)
Rhythm: swing
Tempo: medium (♩ = 108)

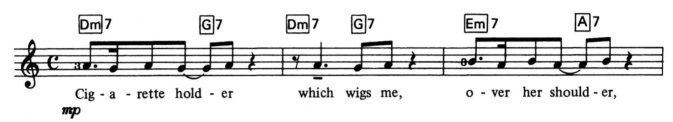

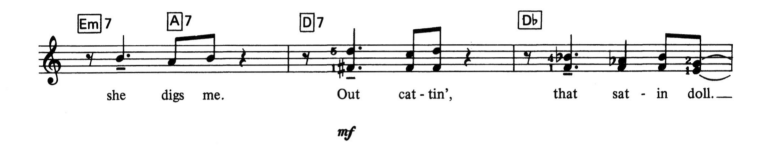

Cig - a - rette hold - er   which wigs me,   o - ver her should - er,

she   digs me.   Out   cat - tin',   that   sat - in   doll. __

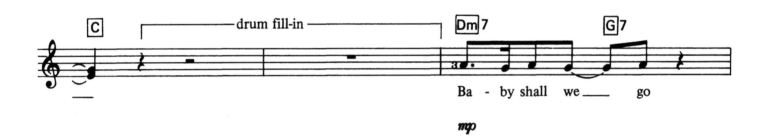

Ba - by shall we __ go

out   skip - pin',   care - ful a - mi - go,   you're   flip - pin',

speaks   Lat - in,   that   sat - in   doll __

add trumpet | Gm7 | C7 | Gm7 | C7

She's no-bo-dy's fool,— so I'm play - ing it cool — as can be.
mp

F | Am7 | D7

I'll give it a whirl,— but I ain't —
cresc.

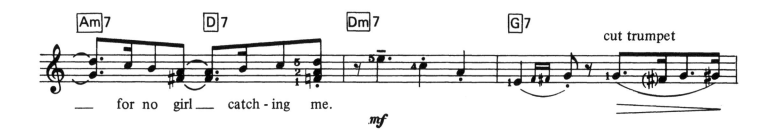

Am7 | D7 | Dm7 | G7 | cut trumpet

— for no girl — catch - ing me.
mf

Dm7 | G7 | Dm7 | G7 | Em7 | A7 | Em7 | A7

Tel - e - phone num - bers, well, you know, do - ing my rhum - bas, with u - no,
mp

D7 | Db | C | drum fill-in

and that 'n', my sat - in doll. —
mf

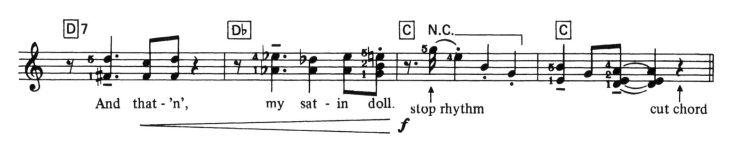

D7 | Db | C N.C. | C

And that - 'n', my sat - in doll. stop rhythm cut chord
f

WAVE

Words & Music by Antonio Carlos Jobim

Suggested registration: jazz guitar (with sustain)
Rhythm: bossa nova
Tempo: medium (♩ = 126)
Synchro-start on

So close your eyes, _____ for that's a love - ly way to be _____
don't try to fight the ris - ing sea, _____

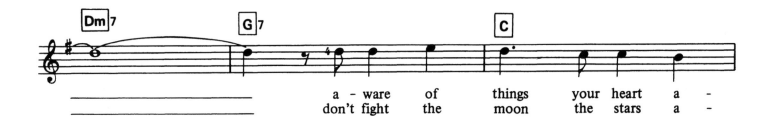

a - ware of things your heart a -
don't fight the moon the stars a -

lone was meant to see.
bove, and don't fight me.
The fun - da - men - tal

lone-li - ness goes when-ev - er two can dream a dream to - ge - ther. _____

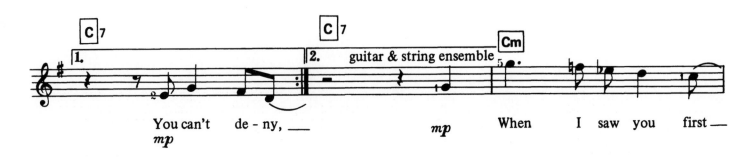

1. You can't de - ny, _____
2. guitar & string ensemble When I saw you first _____

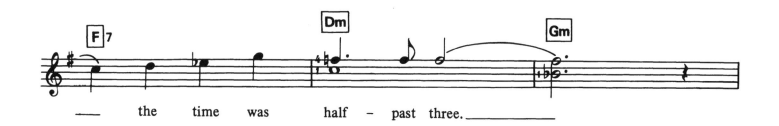

the time was half – past three.

When your eyes met .mine___ it was e – ter – ni – ty.___

cresc. *mf*

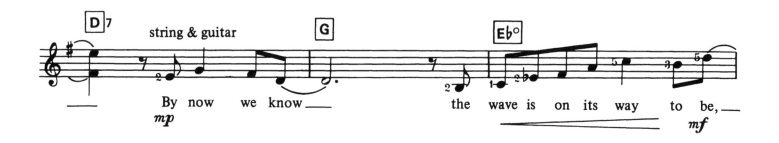

string & guitar

By now we know___ the wave is on its way to be,___

mp *mf*

_____ just catch the wave, don't be a –

fraid of lov – ing me. The fun – da – men – tal

lone – li – ness goes, when – ev – er two can dream a dream to – geth – er.___ stop rhythm

MOONGLOW

Words & Music by Will Hudson, Eddie de Lange & Irving Mills

Suggested registration: string ensemble
Rhythm: swing
Tempo: fairly slow (♩ = 84)

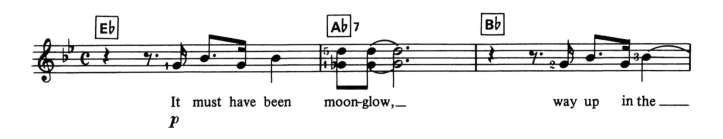

It must have been moon-glow,— way up in the ___

blue. It must have been moon-glow, ___

that led me straight to you.— I still hear you

say - ing, ___ "Dear one, hold me fast."

And I start in pray-ing, ___ Oh Lord, please

add trombone

F7   Bb   Bb7   A7   Ab7   G7

let this last.___ We   seemed to float right through the   air.___

f

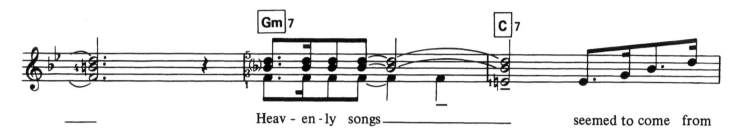

Gm7   C7

___   Heav - en - ly songs_____   seemed to come   from

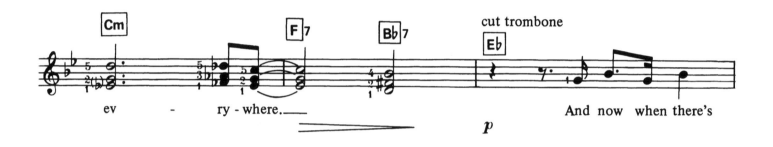

Cm   F7   Bb7   cut trombone
                   Eb

ev -   ry - where.___   And now when there's

p

Ab7   Bb   C7

moon-glow,___   way up   in the   blue.

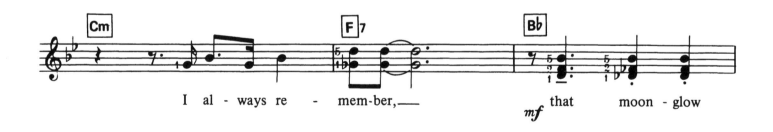

Cm   F7   Bb

I   al - ways re -   mem-ber,___   that   moon - glow

mf

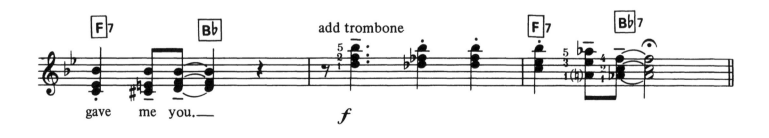

F7   Bb   add trombone   F7   Bb7

gave   me you.___   f

A FINE ROMANCE

Music by Jerome Kern. Words by Dorothy Fields

Suggested registration: piano
Rhythm: swing
Tempo: fast (♩ = 168)
Synchro-start on

A fine ro - mance! With

no kiss - es! A fine

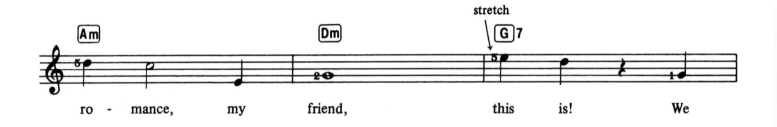

ro - mance, my friend, this is! We

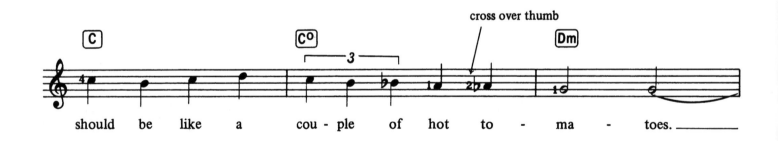

should be like a cou - ple of hot to - ma - toes. _____

_____ But you're as cold as yes - ter - day's mashed po -

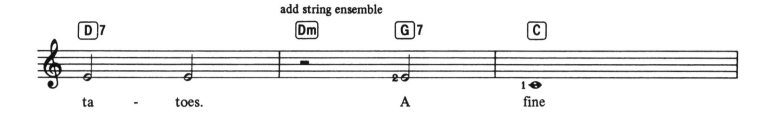

ta - toes.　　　A　fine

ro - mance!　You　won't　nest - le.　A

fine　　　ro - mance,　you　won't

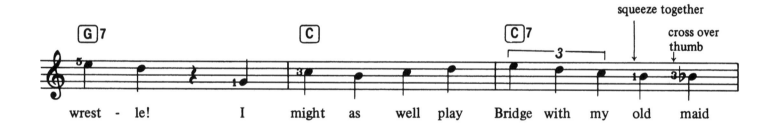

wrest - le!　I　might　as　well　play　Bridge　with　my　old　maid

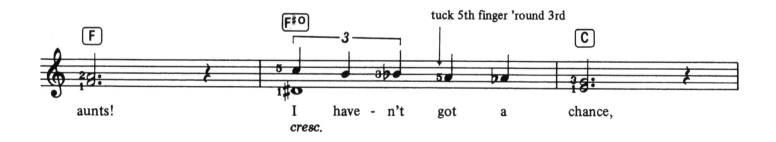

aunts!　I　have - n't　got　a　chance,

cresc.

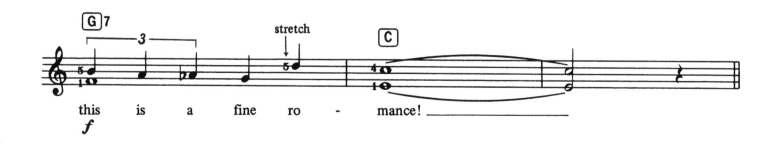

this　is　a　fine　ro - mance!

f

THEY DIDN'T BELIEVE ME

Music by Jerome Kern. Words by Herbert Reynolds

Suggested registration: piano
Rhythm: beguine (or rhumba)
Tempo: medium (♩ = 108)
Synchro-start on

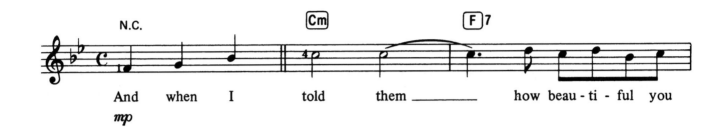

And when I told them _____ how beau - ti - ful you

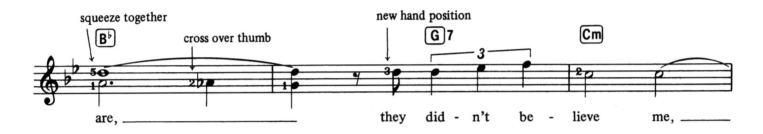

are, _____ they did - n't be - lieve me, _____

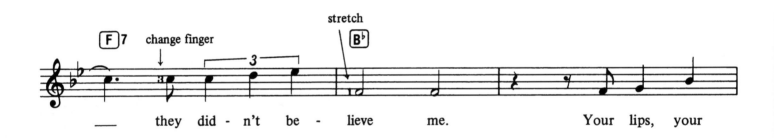

_____ they did - n't be - lieve me. Your lips, your

eyes, your cheeks, your hair are in a class be - yond com -

pare. You're the love - li - est girl _____ that one could

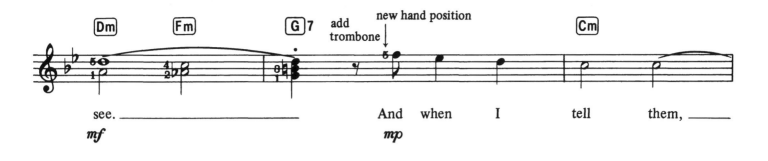

see. _____ And when I tell them, _____

mf   *mp*

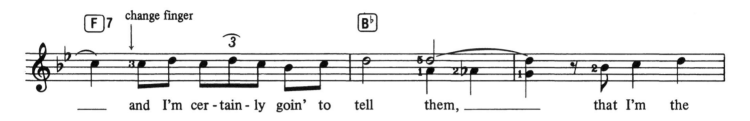

_____ and I'm cer-tain-ly goin' to tell them, _____ that I'm the

man   whose wife one day you'll be, _____

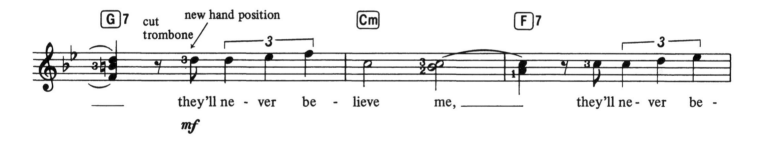

_____ they'll ne - ver be - lieve me, _____ they'll ne - ver be -

mf

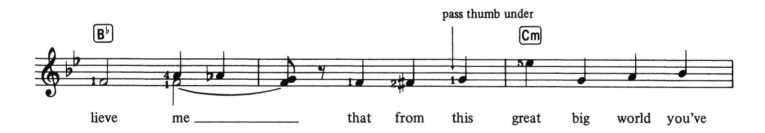

lieve me _____ that from this great big world you've

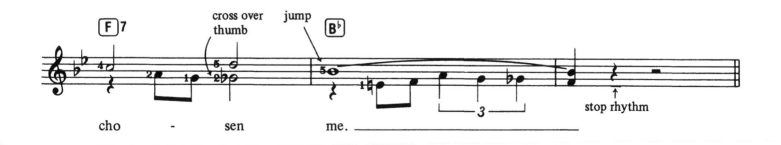

cho - sen me. _____

ALL THE THINGS YOU ARE

Music by Jerome Kern. Words by Oscar Hammerstein II

Suggested registration: guitar
Rhythm: bossa nova
Tempo: medium (♩ = 108)

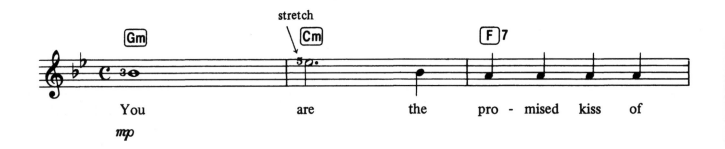

You are the pro - mised kiss of

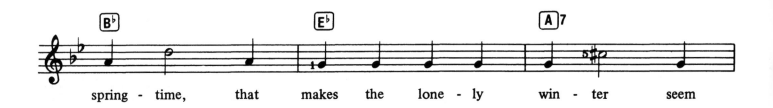

spring - time, that makes the lone - ly win - ter seem

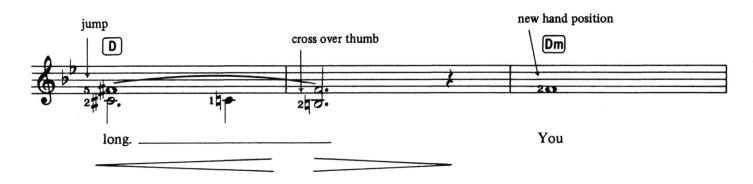

long. _____ You

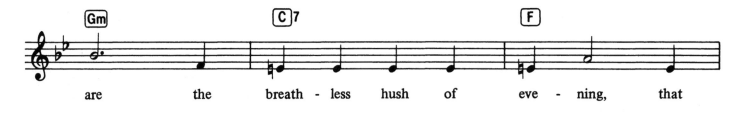

are the breath - less hush of eve - ning, that

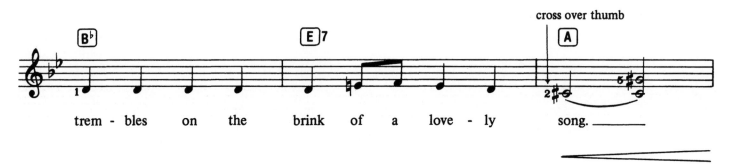

trem - bles on the brink of a love - ly song. _____

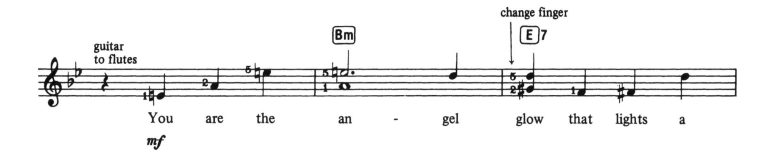

You are the an - gel glow that lights a

star, _____ the dear - est things I

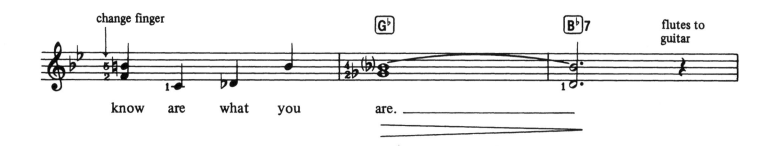

know are what you are. _____

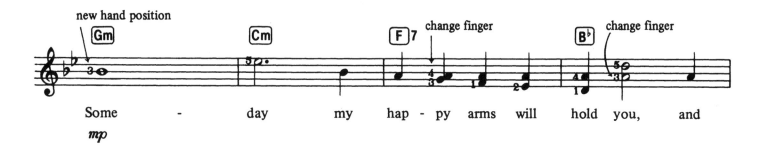

Some - day my hap - py arms will hold you, and

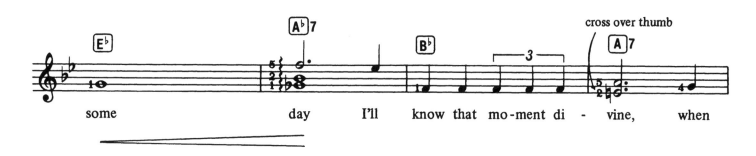

some day I'll know that mo - ment di - vine, when

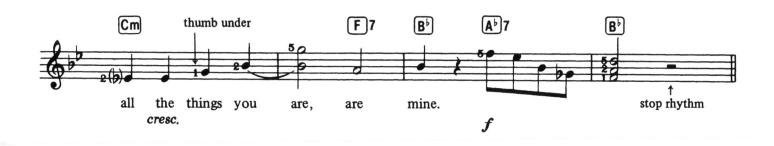

all the things you are, are mine.

ALL I HAVE TO DO IS DREAM

Words & Music by Boudleaux Bryant

Suggested registration: string ensemble
Rhythm: rock
Tempo: medium (♩ = 112)

mf Dream, _____ dream, dream, dream, ___ dream, _____

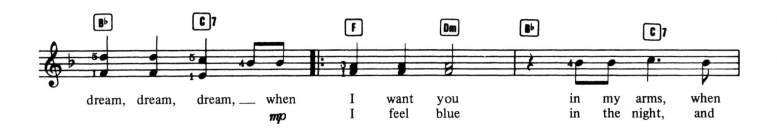

dream, dream, dream, ___ when
mp I want you I feel blue in my arms, when in the night, and

I want you
I need you and all your charms, when - ev - er I want you ___
to hold me tight, when - ev - er I want you ___

1.
all I have to do is dream. _____ Dream, dream, dream, when
all I have to do is

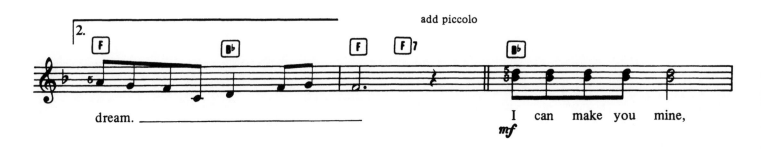

2.   add piccolo
dream. _____ I can make you mine,
mf

taste your lips of wine. An - y - time, night or day.

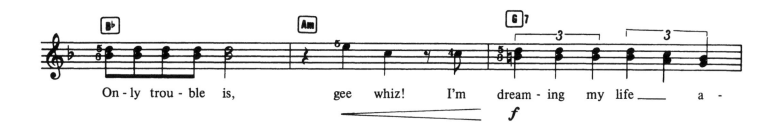

On - ly trou - ble is, gee whiz! I'm dream - ing my life ___ a -

f

- way! ___ I need you so, that I could die, I

mp

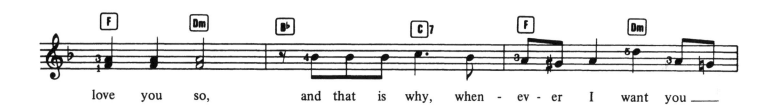

love you so, and that is why, when - ev - er I want you ___

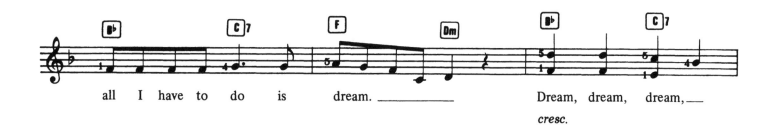

all I have to do is dream. ___ Dream, dream, dream, ___

cresc.

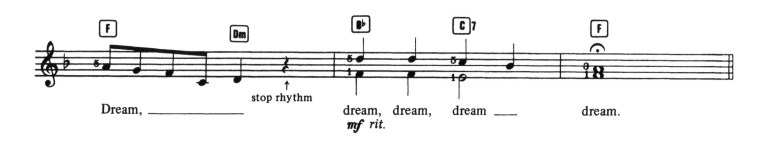

Dream, _____ stop rhythm dream, dream, dream ___ dream.

mf rit.

BYE BYE LOVE

Words & Music by Felice & Boudleaux Bryant

Suggested registration: jazz organ (with tremolo)
Rhythm: rock
Tempo: quite fast (♩ = 160)
Synchro-start on

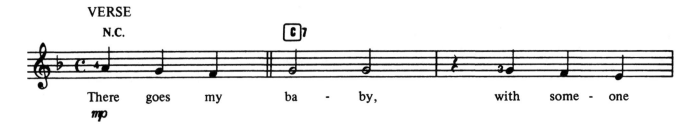

There goes my ba - by, with some - one

new. She sure looks hap - py,

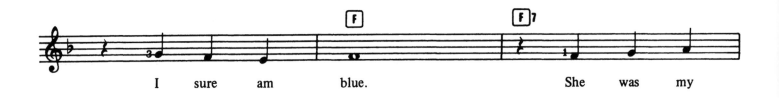

I sure am blue. She was my

ba - by, _____ till he stepped in.

Good - bye to ro - mance that might have

been. _____ Bye, bye, love.

Bye, bye, hap - pi - ness. ____ Hel - lo

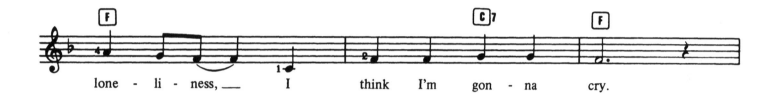

lone - li - ness, ___ I think I'm gon - na cry.

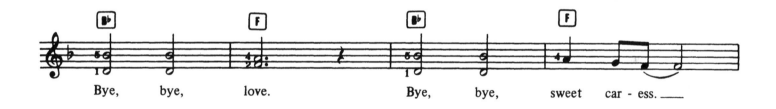

Bye, bye, love. Bye, bye, sweet car - ess. ___

Hel - lo emp - ti - ness, ___ I feel like I could

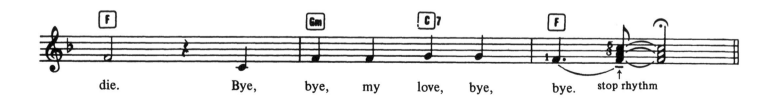

die. Bye, bye, my love, bye, bye. stop rhythm

FUNNY, FAMILIAR, FORGOTTEN FEELINGS

Words & Music by Mickey Newbury

Suggested registration: guitar. Arpeggio if available
Rhythm: waltz
Tempo: medium (♩ = 92)
Synchro-start on

Last night, qui - et - ly, she walked through my
sad, so sad _____ to watch love go

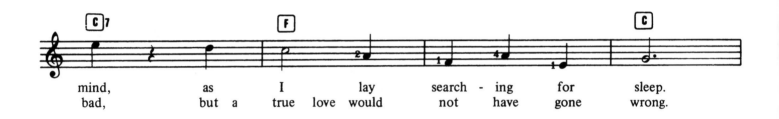

mind, as I lay search - ing for sleep.
bad, but a true love would not have gone wrong.

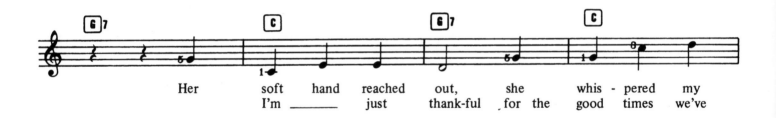

Her soft hand reached out, she whis - pered my
I'm _____ just thank-ful for the good times we've

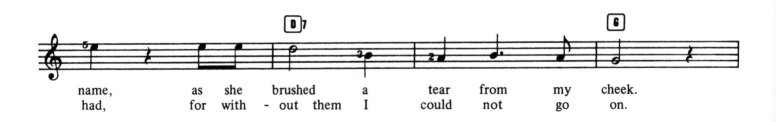

name, as she brushed a tear from my cheek.
had, for with - out them I could not go on.

And then those fun - ny, fa - mil - iar, for - got - ten
With all these fun - ny, fa - mil - iar, for - got - ten

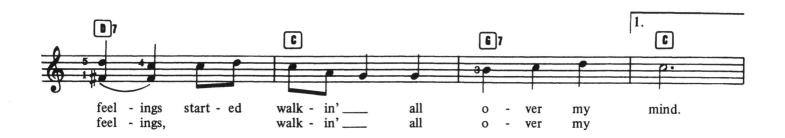

feel - ings start - ed walk - in' ___ all o - ver my mind.
feel - ings, walk - in' ___ all o - ver my

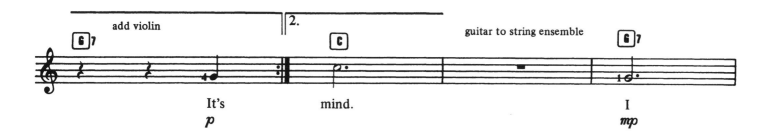

add violin

guitar to string ensemble

It's mind. I

p *mp*

must go on, be ___ strong, tho' a mil - lion

tear - drops may fall. Be - fore these fun - ny, fa -

mf

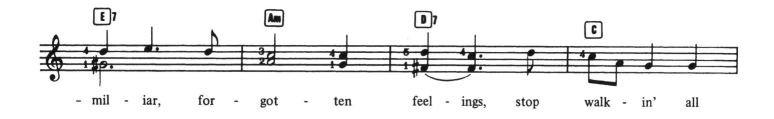

- mil - iar, for - got - ten feel - ings, stop walk - in' all

o - ver my mind.

I CAN'T STOP LOVING YOU

Words & Music by Don Gibson

Suggested registration: string ensemble. Arpeggio if available
Rhythm: swing
Tempo: quite slow (♩ = 92)
Synchro-start on

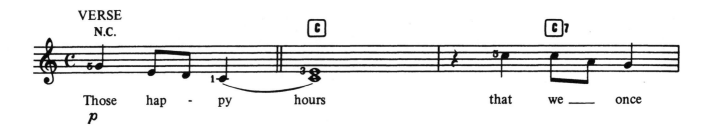

VERSE

N.C.

Those hap - py hours that we ___ once

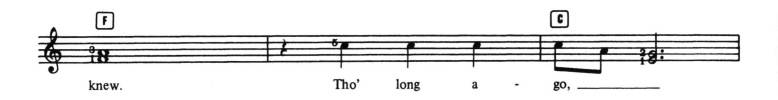

knew. Tho' long a - go, ___

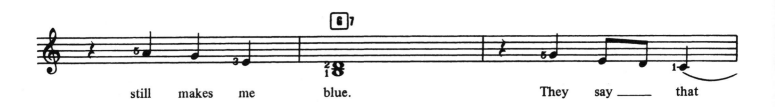

still makes me blue. They say ___ that

time heals a bro - ken heart,

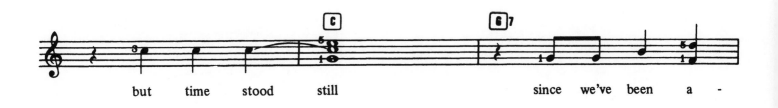

but time stood still since we've been a -

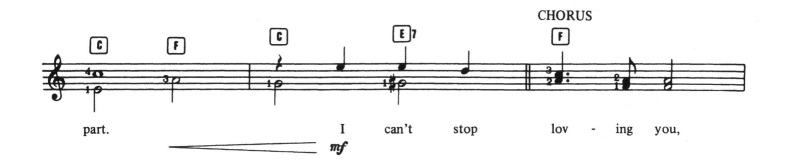

CHORUS

part.   I can't stop lov - ing you,

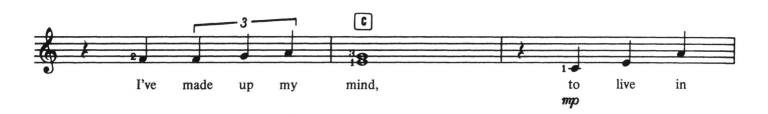

I've made up my mind,   to live in

mem - o - ry   of old lone - some times.

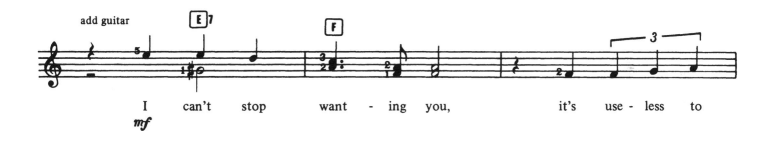

add guitar

I can't stop want - ing you,   it's use - less to

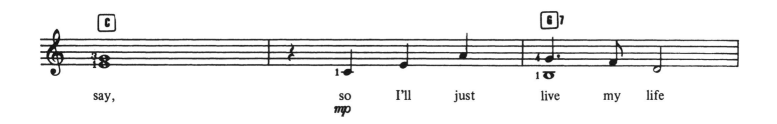

say,   so I'll just live my life

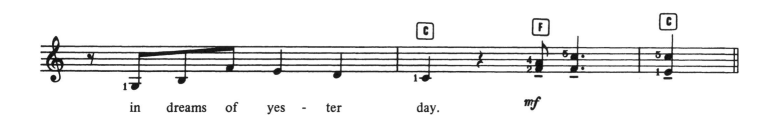

in dreams of yes - ter day.

TAKE THESE CHAINS FROM MY HEART

Words & Music by Fred Rose & Hy Heath

Suggested registration: Hawaiian guitar
Rhythm: swing
Tempo: medium (♩ = 104)
Synchro-start on

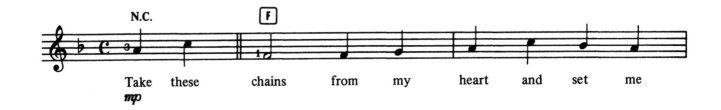

Take these chains from my heart and set me

mp

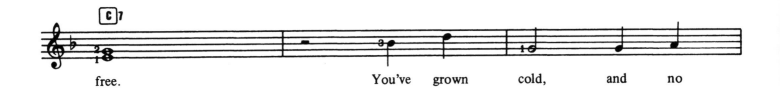

free. You've grown cold, and no

lon - ger care for me. All my

cresc.

faith in you is gone, but the heart - aches lin - ger

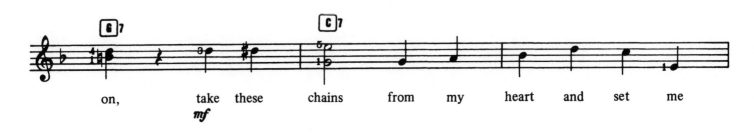

on, take these chains from my heart and set me

mf

free.

Take these tears from my

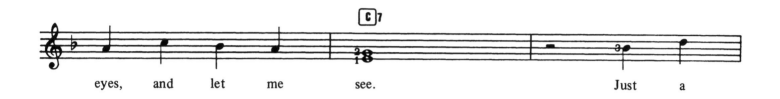

eyes, and let me see.

Just a

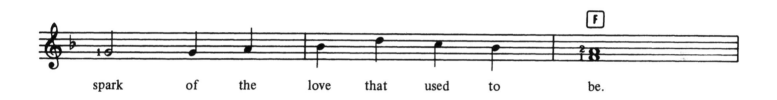

spark of the love that used to be.

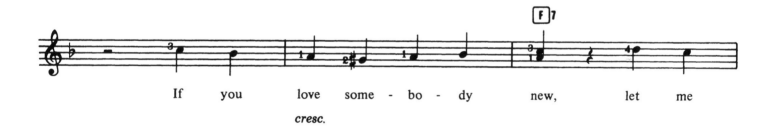

If you love some - bo - dy new, let me

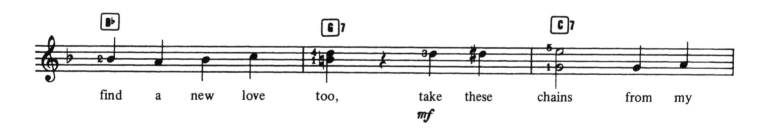

find a new love too, take these chains from my

heart and set me free.

ONE MOMENT IN TIME

Words & Music by Albert Hammond & John Bettis

Suggested registration: string ensemble
Rhythm: rock
Tempo: medium (♩ = 92)

Each day I live I want to be a day to

mp

give the best of me. I'm on-ly one, but not a -

lone, my fi-nest day is yet un-known. I broke my

heart for ev-'ry gain, to taste the sweet, I faced the

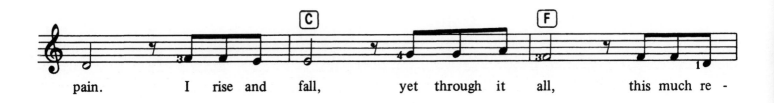

pain. I rise and fall, yet through it all, this much re -

CHORUS

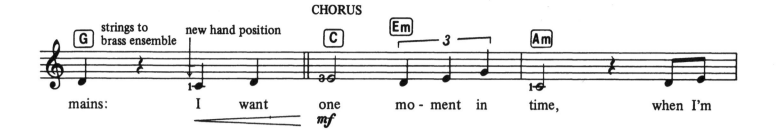

mains: I want one mo - ment in time, when I'm

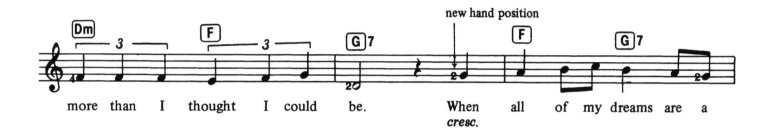

more than I thought I could be. When all of my dreams are a

heart - beat a - way, and the ans - wers are all up to me. Give me

one mo - ment in time, when I'm rac - ing with des - ti -

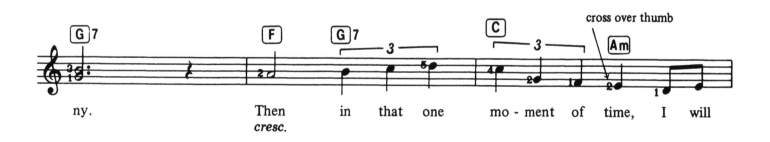

ny.   Then in that one mo - ment of time, I will

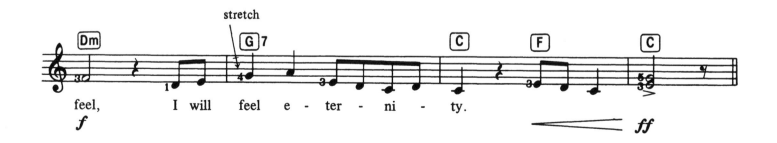

feel, I will feel e - ter - ni - ty.

THE WIND BENEATH MY WINGS

Words & Music by Jeff Silbar & Larry Henley

Suggested registration: guitar
Rhythm: rock
Tempo: medium (♩ = 120)

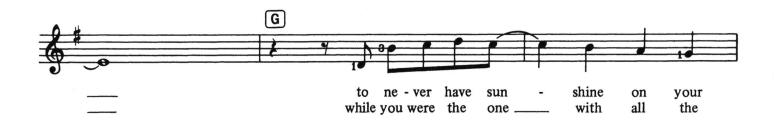

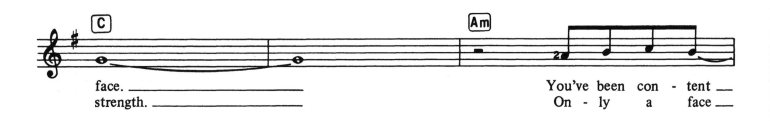

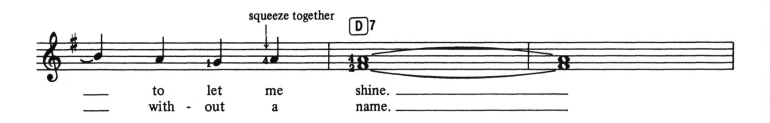

CHORUS

Did you ev-er know___ that you're my

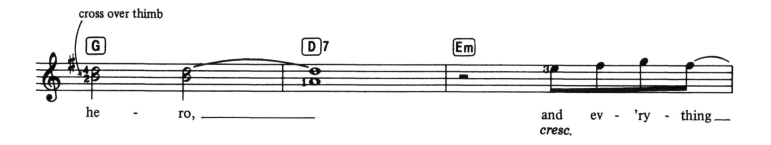

he - ro, ___ and ev - 'ry - thing ___

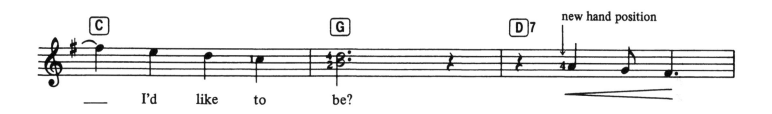

___ I'd like to be?

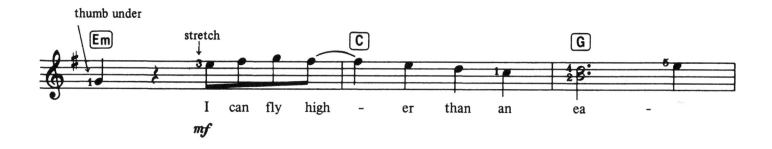

I can fly high - er than an ea -

gle, ___ 'cause you are the wind ___ be - neath my

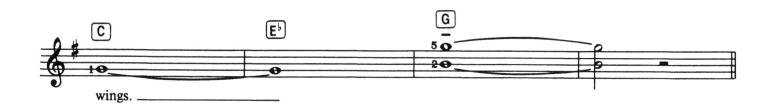

wings. ___

SOMEWHERE OUT THERE

Words & Music by James Horner, Barry Mann & Cynthia Weil

Suggested registration: clarinet
Rhythm: rock
Tempo: medium (♩ = 96)

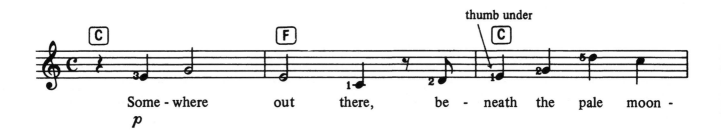

Some - where out there, be - neath the pale moon -

light. Some - one's think - in' of me, and

lov - ing me to - night. _____ Some - where _____

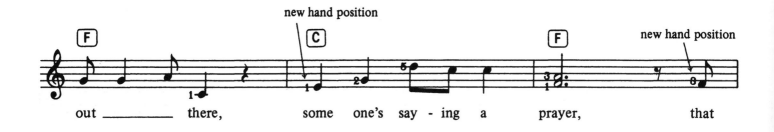

out _____ there, some one's say - ing a prayer, that

we'll find one an - oth - er, in that big some - where _____ out _____

there. And ev-en though I know how ve-ry far a-part we are,____ it

helps to think we might be wish-in' on the same bright star. And

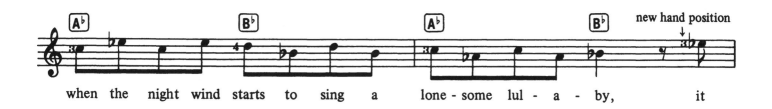

when the night wind starts to sing a lone-some lul-a-by, it

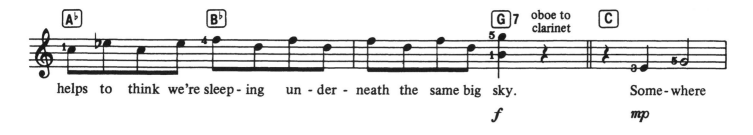

helps to think we're sleep-ing un-der-neath the same big sky. Some-where

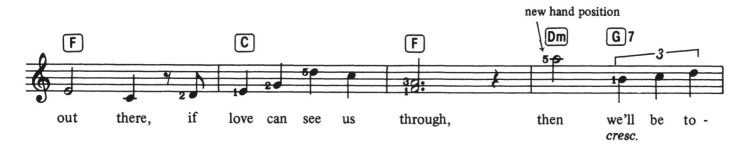

out there, if love can see us through, then we'll be to-

ge-ther some-where out there, out where dreams come true.____

RIGHT HERE WAITING

Words & Music by Richard Marx

Suggested registration: horn
Rhythm: rock
Tempo: quite slow (♩ = 88)

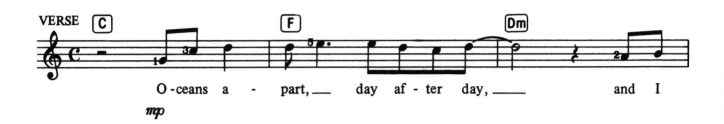

VERSE C   F   Dm

O-ceans a - part, __ day af - ter day, __ and I

G7   C   F

slow - ly go in - sane, __ I hear your voice __ on the line,

Dm   G7   Am   change finger

but it does - n't stop the pain. If I see you next
Oh can't you see __

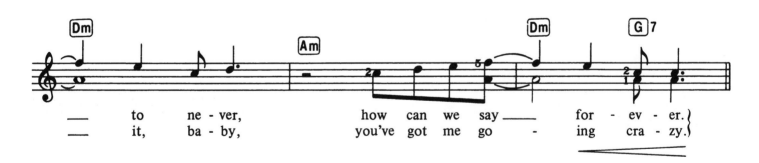

Dm   Am   Dm   G7

to ne - ver, how can we say __ for - ev - er.
it, ba - by, you've got me go - ing cra - zy.

CHORUS

C   horn to synth.   G7   Am

When - ev - er you go, __ what - ev - er you do, __ I will be

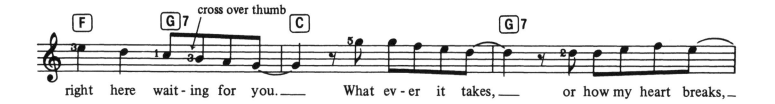

right here wait-ing for you. ___ What ev-er it takes, ___ or how my heart breaks, ___

___ I will be right here wait-ing for you. ___ I won-der

how we can sur-vive ___ this ro - mance. ___

But in the end if I'm with you ___ I'll take the chance.

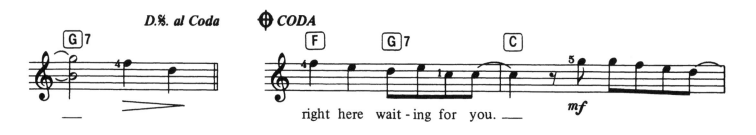

right here wait-ing for you. ___

ANOTHER DAY IN PARADISE

Words & Music by Phil Collins

Suggested registration: flute
Rhythm: rock
Tempo: medium (♩ = 104)

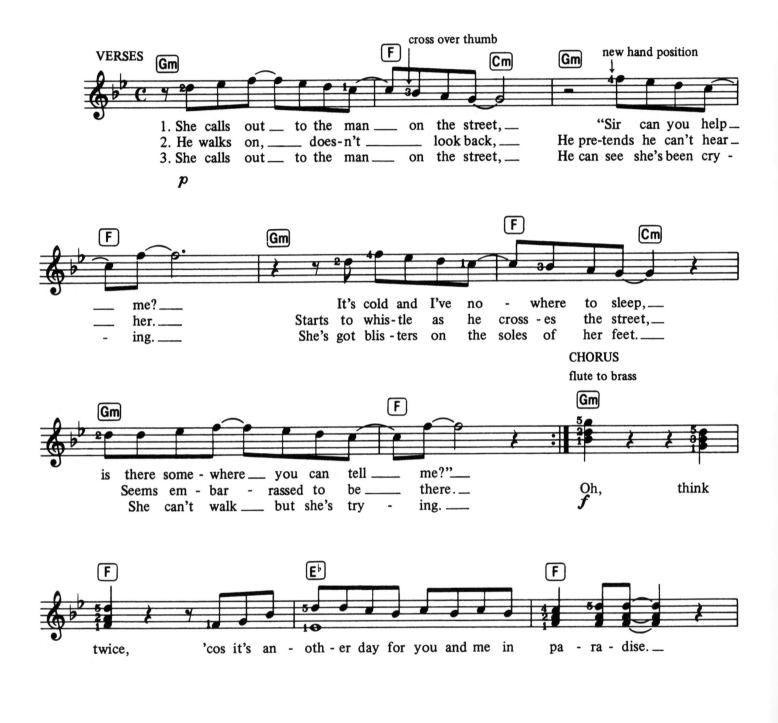

1. She calls out to the man on the street, "Sir can you help me?
2. He walks on, doesn't look back, He pretends he can't hear her.
3. She calls out to the man on the street, He can see she's been cry-ing.

It's cold and I've no-where to sleep, is there some-where you can tell me?"
Starts to whis-tle as he cross-es the street, Seems em-bar-rassed to be there.
She's got blis-ters on the soles of her feet. She can't walk but she's try-ing.

CHORUS
flute to brass

Oh, think twice, 'cos it's an-oth-er day for you and me in pa-ra-dise.

Oh, think twice, 'cos it's an oth-er day for you,

new hand position · INTERLUDE change finger

you and me in pa - ra - dise. *mp* Just think a -

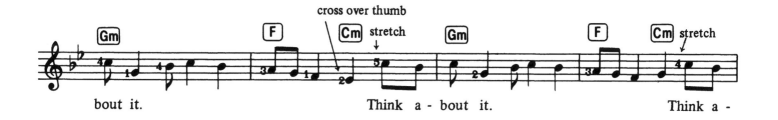

cross over thumb

bout it. Think a - bout it. Think a -

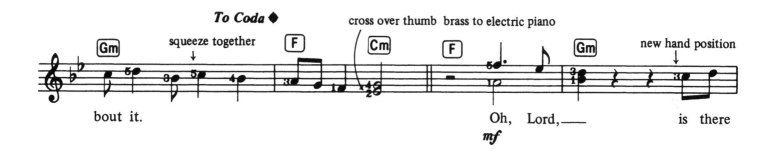

To Coda ◆ squeeze together cross over thumb brass to electric piano new hand position

bout it. Oh, Lord, ____ is there
mf

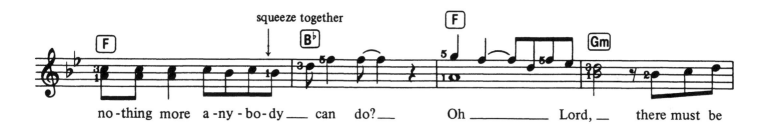

squeeze together

no - thing more a - ny - bo - dy ____ can do? ____ Oh ____ Lord, ____ there must be

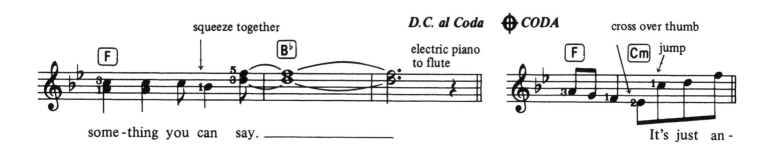

squeeze together *D.C. al Coda* ⊕ *CODA* cross over thumb

electric piano to flute

some - thing you can say. ____ It's just an -

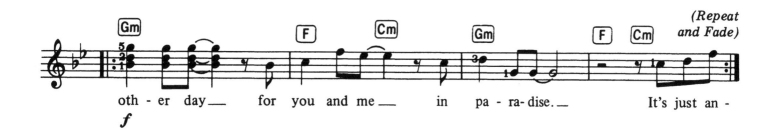

(Repeat and Fade)

oth - er day ____ for you and me ____ in pa - ra - dise. ____ It's just an -
f

THE FOOL ON THE HILL

Words & Music by John Lennon & Paul McCartney

Suggested registration: flute
Rhythm: rock
Tempo: medium (♩ = 92)

1. Day af - ter day, _____ a - lone on a

p

hill, the man with the fool - ish grin is keep - ing

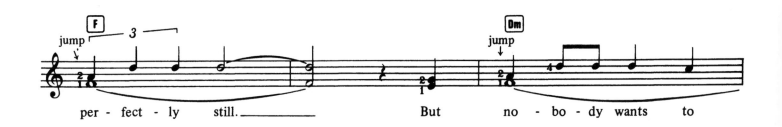

per - fect - ly still. _____ But no - bo - dy wants to

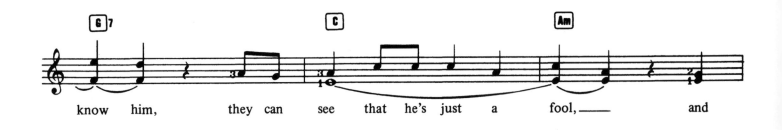

know him, they can see that he's just a fool, _____ and

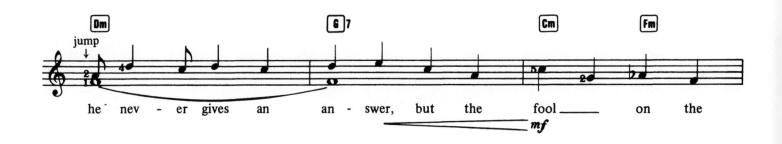

he nev - er gives an an - swer, but the fool _____ on the

mf

hill   sees   the   sun   go - ing   down,   and   the

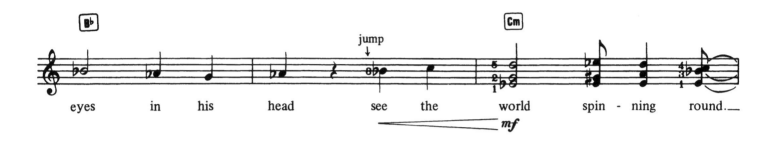

eyes   in   his   head   see   the   world   spin - ning   round.___

2. Well on the way, head in a cloud,
   The man of a thousand voices talking perfectly loud.
   But nobody ever hears him, or the sound he appears to make,
   And he never seems to notice, but the fool on the hill

   Sees the sun going down, and the eyes in his head
   See the world spinning round.

3. *(Instrumental solo for 4 bars)*

   And nobody seems to like him, they can tell what he wants to do,
   And he never shows his feelings, but the fool on the hill

   See the sun going down, *(etc.)*

4. *(Instrumental solo for 4 bars)*

   He never listens to them, he knows that they're the fools
   They don't like him, the fool on the hill

   Sees the sun going down, *(etc.)*

HOLDING BACK THE YEARS

Words by Mick Hucknall. Music by Mick Hucknall/Neil Moss

Suggested registration: string ensemble
Rhythm: rock
Tempo: medium (♩ = 112)

VERSES

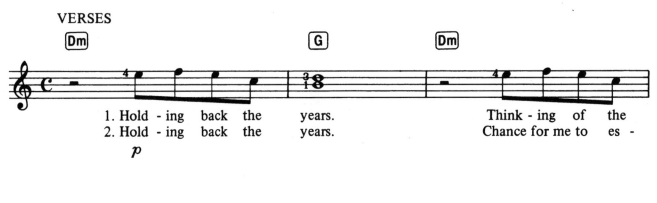

1. Hold - ing back the years. Think - ing of the
2. Hold - ing back the years. Chance for me to es -

fear I've had ___ so long. When some - bo - dy ___ hears, ___
cape from all ___ I know. Hold - ing back the ___ tears, ___

list - en to the fear that's gone. ___
no - thing here has grown. ___

add flute

Stran - gled by the wish - es of pa - ter, hop - ing for the
I've wast - ed all my tears. Wast - ed all those

arms of ma - ter. Get to meet her soon - er or la - ter. ___
years. ___

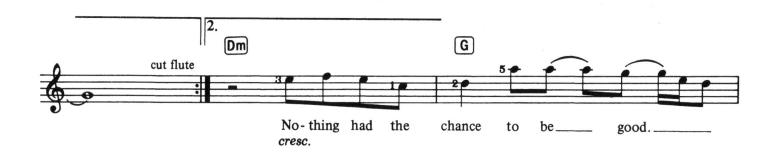

No- thing had the chance to be____ good._____

No- thing ev - er could,___ yeah, _____ Oh _____ well

CHORUS

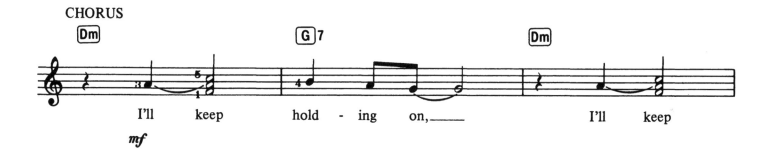

I'll keep hold - ing on,_____ I'll keep

hold - ing on,_____ I'll keep hold - ing on,_____

D.S. (Repeat CHORUS and Fade for ending)

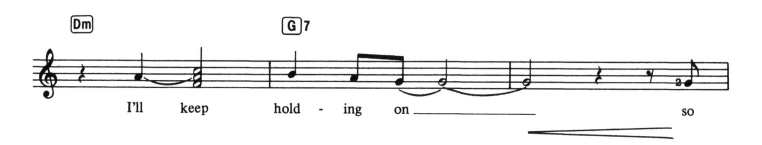

I'll keep hold - ing on _____ so

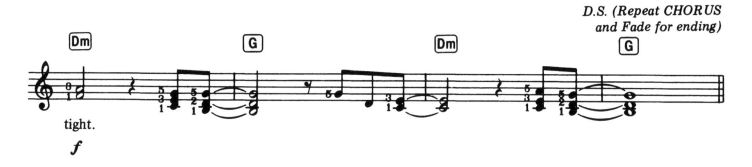

tight.

I CAN SEE CLEARLY NOW

Words & Music by Johnny Nash

Suggested registration: flute
Rhythm: rock
Tempo: medium (♩ = 112)

CHORUS

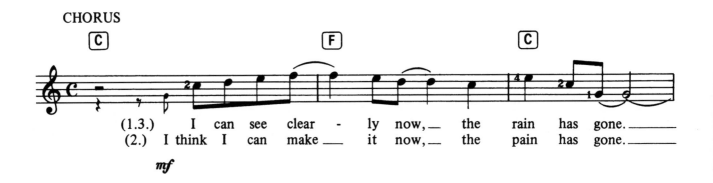

(1.3.) I can see clear - ly now, the rain has gone.
(2.) I think I can make it now, the pain has gone.

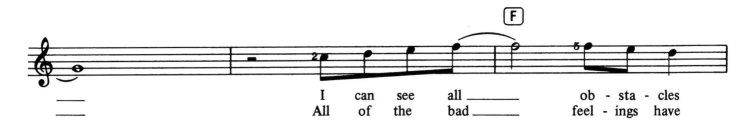

I can see all ob - sta - cles
All of the bad feel - ings have

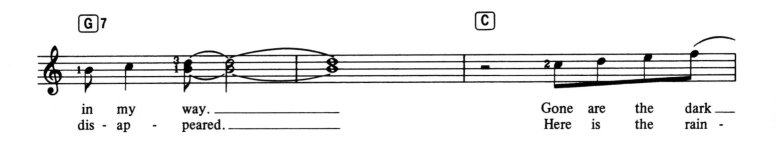

in my way. Gone are the dark
dis - ap - peared. Here is the rain -

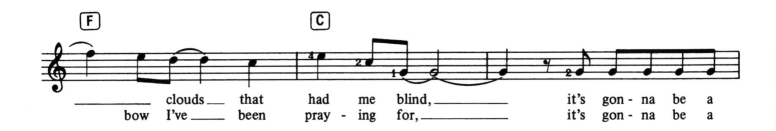

clouds that had me blind, it's gon - na be a
bow I've been pray - ing for, it's gon - na be a

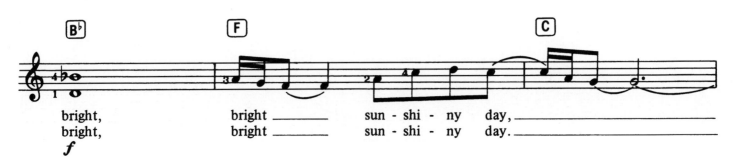

bright, bright sun - shi - ny day,
bright, bright sun - shi - ny day.

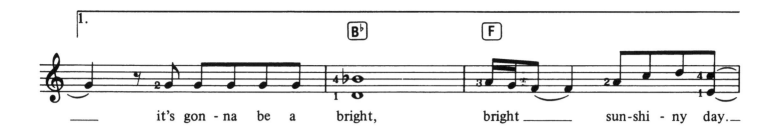

it's gon - na be a bright, bright _____ sun-shi - ny day._____

INTERLUDE

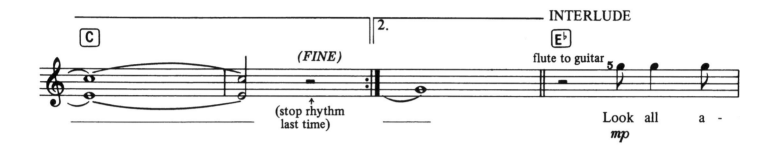

(FINE)

(stop rhythm last time)

flute to guitar

Look all a -

mp

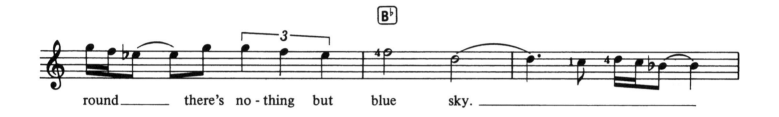

round_____ there's no - thing but blue sky. _____

Look straight a - head,_____ no - thing but blue sky._____

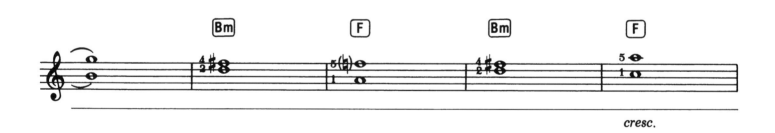

cresc.

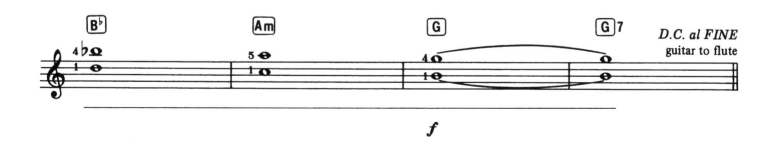

D.C. al FINE
guitar to flute

f

A WOMAN IN LOVE

Words & Music by Barry Gibb & Robin Gibb

Suggested registration: flute
Rhythm: rock
Tempo: medium (♩ = 96)

CHORUS

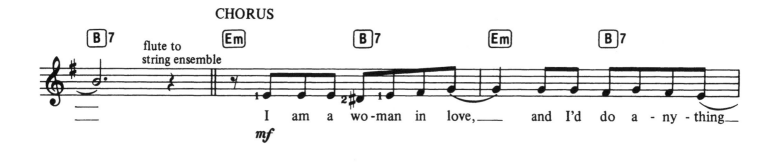

I am a wo-man in love,___ and I'd do a-ny-thing___

___ to get you in-to my world,___ and hold you with-in.___ It's a

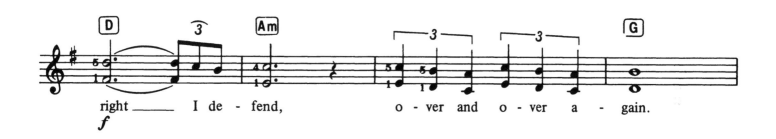

right ___ I de - fend, o - ver and o - ver a - gain.

What do I do? I am a wo-man in love,___ and I'm talk-in' to you,___

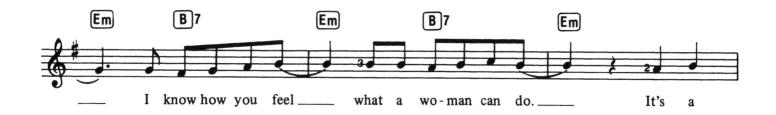

___ I know how you feel ___ what a wo-man can do.___ It's a

right ___ I de - fend, o - ver and o - ver a - gain.

(Repeat and fade)

MISSING YOU

Words & Music by Chris De Burgh

Suggested registration: piano
Rhythm: rock
Tempo: medium (♩ = 104)

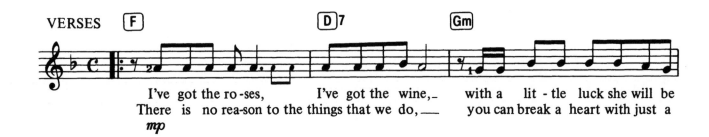

VERSES

mp

I've got the ro-ses, I've got the wine, with a lit-tle luck she will be
There is no rea-son to the things that we do, you can break a heart with just a

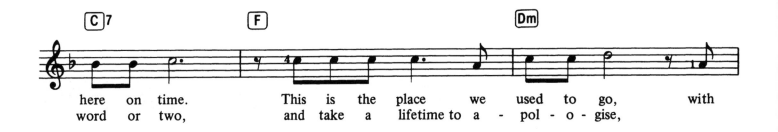

here on time. This is the place we used to go, with
word or two, and take a lifetime to a - pol - o - gise,

ro - man - tic mu-sic and the lights — down low. — And as you stand there a - mazed at the
when the one you love's — in - front of your eyes, — And I will fall to my knees like a

mf

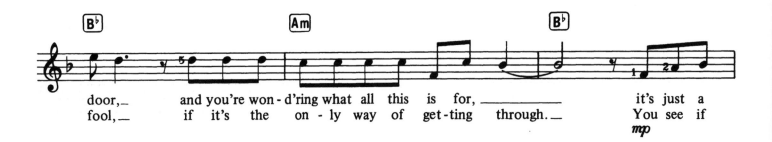

door, — and you're won - d'ring what all this is for, _____ it's just a
fool, — if it's the on - ly way of get - ting through. — You see if

mp

sim - ple thing from me to you, the la - dy that I a - dore. _____ 'Cause there's
I ___ think you are beau-ti - ful, some-one else is gon-na feel it too. — So there's

cresc.

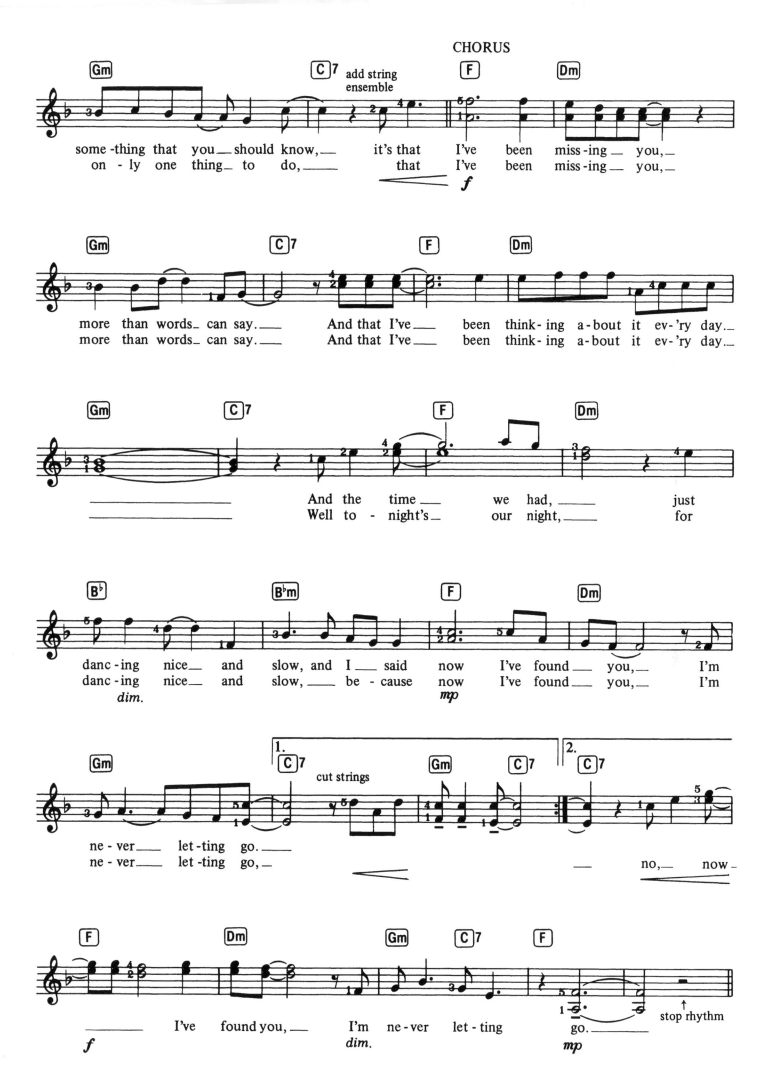

FROM A DISTANCE

Words & Music by Julie Gold

Suggested registration: electric piano
Rhythm: rock
Tempo: fairly slow (♩ = 84)

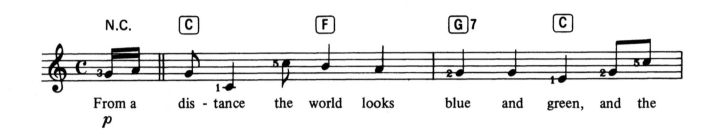

From a dis - tance the world looks blue and green, and the

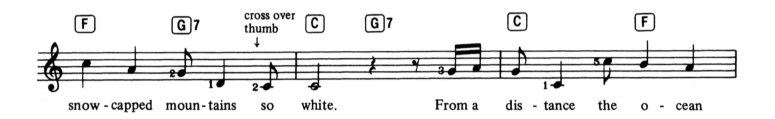

snow - capped moun - tains so white. From a dis - tance the o - cean

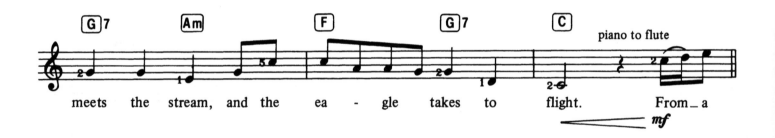

meets the stream, and the ea - gle takes to flight. From _ a

dis - tance there _ is har - mo - ny, and it e - choes through _ the

land. _ It's the voice of hope, _ it's the voice of peace, _ it's the

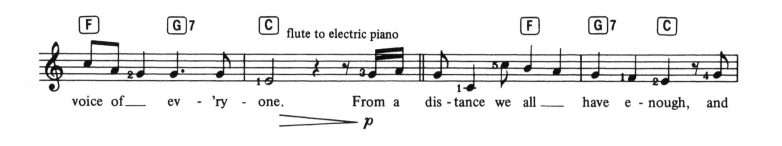

voice of___ ev - 'ry - one. From a dis - tance we all ___ have e - nough, and

p

no - one is ___ in need. There are no guns, no bombs, and no di - sease, no

hun - gry mouths to feed. For ___ a mo - ment we must be in - stru - ments, march - ing

f

in a com - mon band. ___ Play - ing songs of hope, ___ play - ing songs of peace, ___ they're the

songs of ___ ev - 'ry - one. God ___ is watch - ing us, ___ God ___ is watch - ing us, ___ God ___ is

watch - ing us ___ from a dis - tance.

stop rhythm

HOW AM I SUPPOSED TO LIVE WITHOUT YOU

Words & Music by M. Bolton & D. James

Suggested registration: brass ensemble
Rhythm: rock
Tempo: fairly slow (♩ = 76)

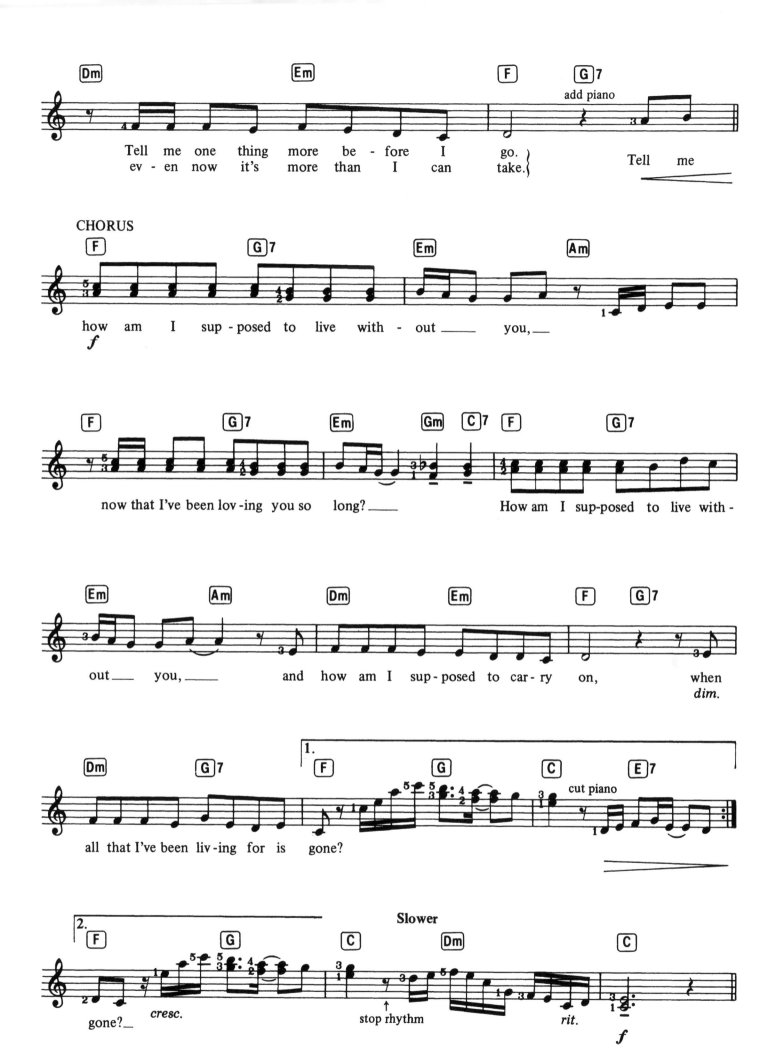

TILL THERE WAS YOU

Words & Music by Meredith Willson

Suggested registration: guitar
Rhythm: rhumba
Tempo: medium (♩ = 100)
Synchro-start on

There were bells on the hill, but I

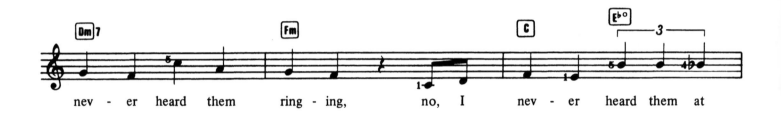

nev - er heard them ring - ing, no, I nev - er heard them at

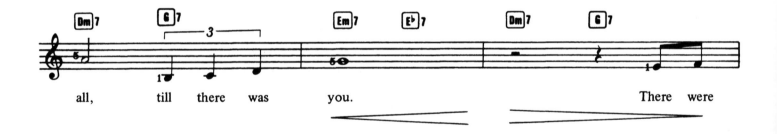

all, till there was you. There were

birds in the sky, but I nev - er saw them

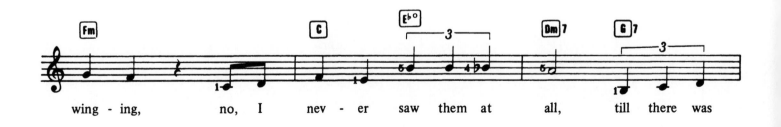

wing - ing, no, I nev - er saw them at all, till there was

you.   And   there   was   mu - sic   and

there   were   won - der - ful   ros -   es,   they   tell   me,   in

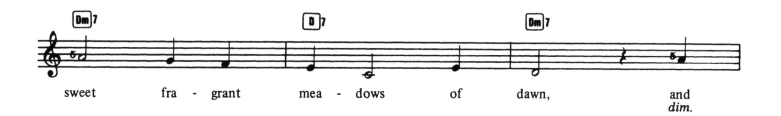

sweet   fra - grant   mea - dows   of   dawn,   and

dew.   There   was   love   all   a - round,   but   I

nev - er   heard   it   sing - ing,   no,   I   nev - er   heard   it   at

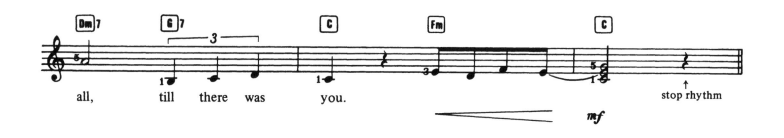

all,   till   there   was   you.

SOMEWHERE

Music by Leonard Bernstein. Lyrics by Stephen Sondheim

Suggested registration: violin solo
Rhythm: rhumba (or bossa nova)
Tempo: slow (♩ = 80)

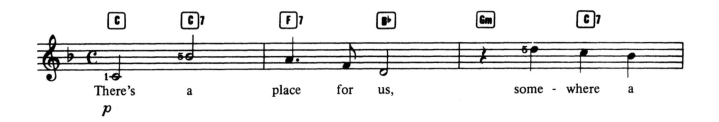

There's a place for us, some - where a

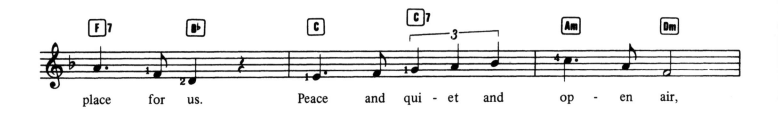

place for us. Peace and qui - et and op - en air,

wait for us some - where. ___ There's a

time for us, some - day a time for us.

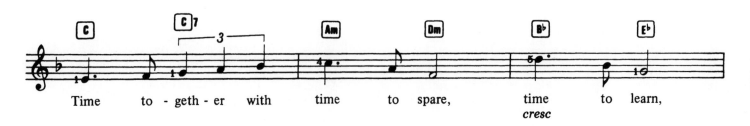

Time to - geth - er with time to spare, time to learn,
cresc

time to care. Some - day. ___ some - where, ___

we'll find a new way of liv - ing, ___ we'll find a way of for -

giv - ing. ___ Some - where. ___

There's a place for us, a time and place for us.

Hold my hand and we're half - way there, hold my hand and I'll take you there.

Some - how, ___ some - day, ___ some - where. _____

stop rhythm

SEVENTY SIX TROMBONES

Words & Music by Meredith Willson

Suggested registration: brass ensemble + trombone
Rhythm: march 6/8
Tempo: medium (♩. = 116)
Synchro-start on

Sev - en - ty six trom -
six trom -

bones led the big pa - rade, with a hun - dred and
bones led the big pa - rade, when the or - der to

ten cor - nets close at hand.
march rang out loud and clear.

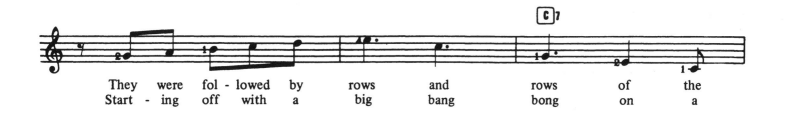

They were fol - lowed by rows and rows of the
Start - ing off with a big bang bong on a

fin - est vir - tu - o - sos, the cream _____ of
Chi - nese gong, by a big _____ bang

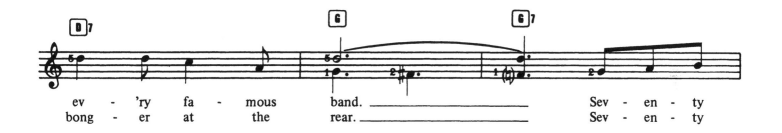

ev - 'ry fa - mous band. _____ Sev - en - ty
bong - er at the rear. _____ Sev - en - ty

six trom - bones caught the morn - ing sun,
six trom - bones hit the coun - ter - point,

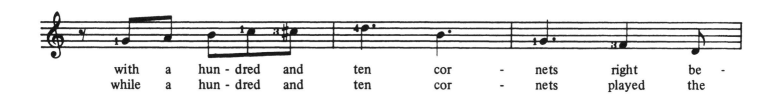

with a hun - dred and ten cor - nets right be -
while a hun - dred and ten cor - nets played the

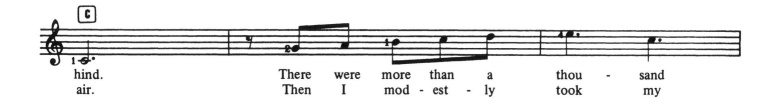

hind. There were more than a thou - sand
air. Then I mod - est - ly took my

reeds spring - ing up like weeds, there were
place as the one and on - ly bass, and I

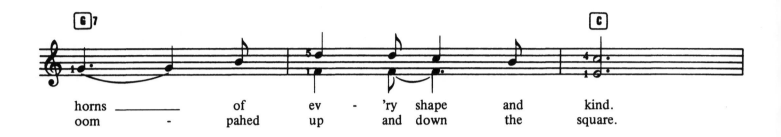

horns _____ of ev - 'ry shape and kind.
oom - pahed up and down the square.

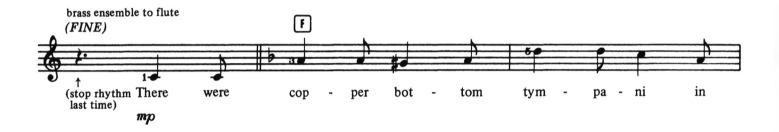

brass ensemble to flute
(FINE)

(stop rhythm There were cop - per bot - tom tym - pa - ni in
last time)
mp

horse pla - toons. f Thun - der - ing,
mp

thun - der - ing, all a - long the way.

Dou - ble bell eu - pho - ni - ums and big bass - soons. _____

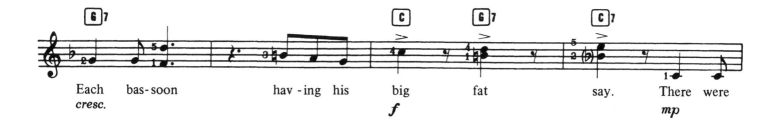

Each bas-soon hav-ing his big fat say. There were
cresc. *f* *mp*

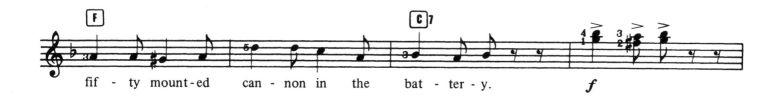

fif - ty mount-ed can - non in the bat - ter - y. *f*

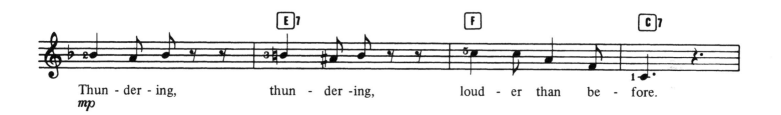

Thun - der - ing, thun - der -ing, loud - er than be - fore.
mp

Cla - ri -nets of ev - 'ry size and trum - pet -ers who'd im - pro - vise a
cresc.

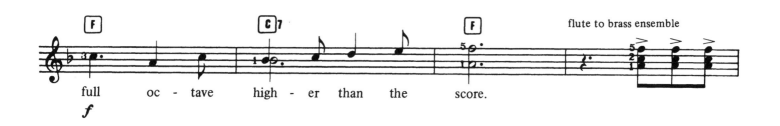

flute to brass ensemble

full oc - tave high - er than the score.
f

D.%. al Fine

Sev - en - ty
mf

73

THE GIRL FROM IPANEMA
(GAROTA DE IPANEMA)

Original Words by Vinicius De Moraes. English Lyric by Norman Gimbel. Music by Antonio Carlos Jobim.

Suggested registration: guitar
Rhythm: bossa nova
Tempo: medium (♩ = 126)

Tall and tan, and young and love - ly, the girl from I - pa -
When she walks she's like a sam - ba, that swings so cool, and

ne - ma goes walk - ing, and when she pass - es, each one she pass - es goes
sways so gen - tle,_____ that when she pass - es, each one she pass - es goes

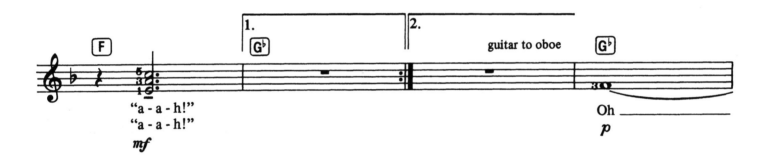

"a - a - h!"
"a - a - h!"

guitar to oboe

Oh _____

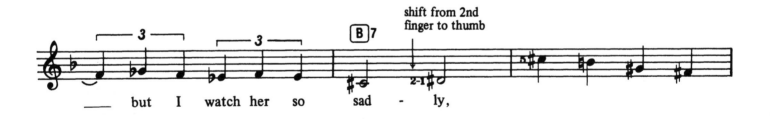

_____ but I watch her so sad - ly,

how _____ can I tell her I love her? _____

*F♯ A C♯

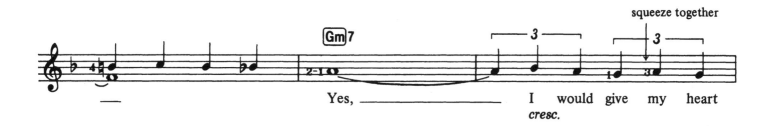

squeeze together

Gm7

Yes, _____ I would give my heart

cresc.

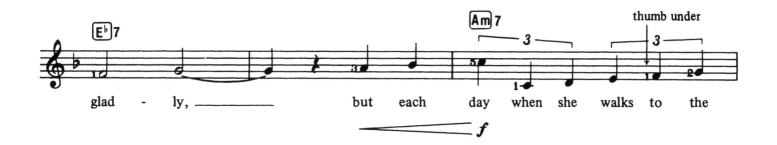

E♭7

thumb under

Am7

glad - ly, _____ but each day when she walks to the

f

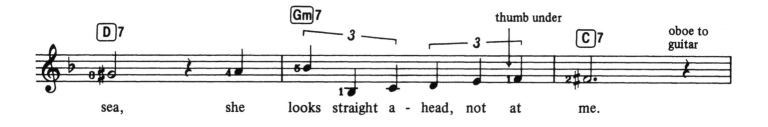

D7

Gm7

thumb under

C7

oboe to guitar

sea, she looks straight a - head, not at me.

F

G7

Tall and tan, and young and love - ly, the girl from I - pa - ne-ma goes walk - ing, and

mp

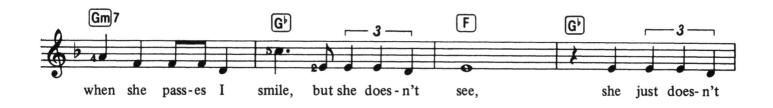

Gm7

G♭

F

G♭

when she pass-es I smile, but she does-n't see, she just does-n't

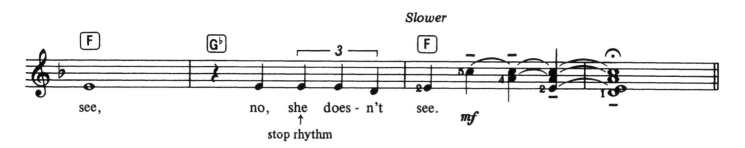

Slower

F

G♭

F

see, no, she does - n't see.

stop rhythm

mf

COME FLY WITH ME

Lyrics by Sammy Cahn. Music by James Van Heusen

Suggested registration: trumpet
Rhythm: swing
Tempo: quite fast (♩ = 152)

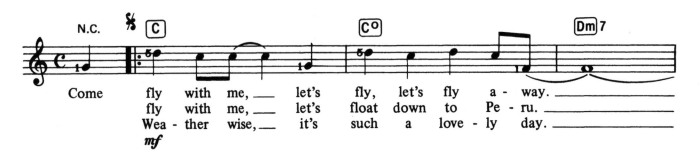

Come fly with me, ___ let's fly, let's fly a - way. ___
fly with me, ___ let's float down to Pe - ru. ___
Wea - ther wise, ___ it's such a love - ly day. ___

If you can use ___ some ex - ot - ic booze, ___ there's a
In Lla - ma land ___ there's a one man band, ___ and he'll
Just say the words ___ and we'll beat the birds ___ down to

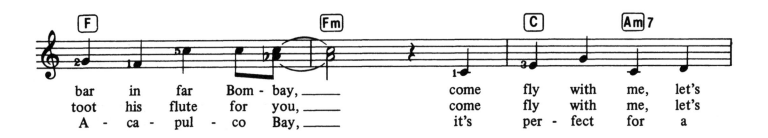

bar in far Bom - bay, ___ come fly with me, let's
toot his flute for you, ___ come fly with me, let's
A - ca - pul - co Bay, ___ it's per - fect for a

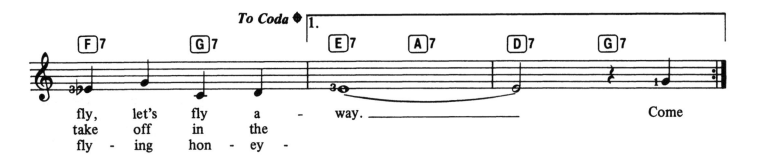

To Coda ◆ **1.**

fly, let's fly a - way. ___ Come
take off in the
fly - ing hon - ey -

2. trumpet to clarinet   thumb under

blue. Once I get you up there,

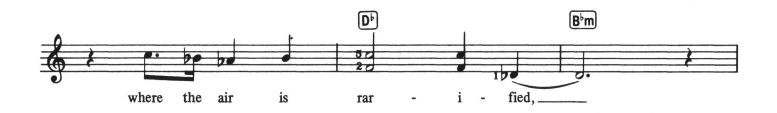

where the air is rar - i - fied, _____

we'll just glide, _____ star - ry eyed.

Once I get you up there, I'll be hold - ing you so near, _

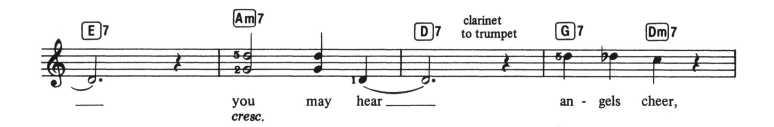

_ you may hear _____ an - gels cheer,
cresc.

D.%. al Coda **⊕** *CODA*

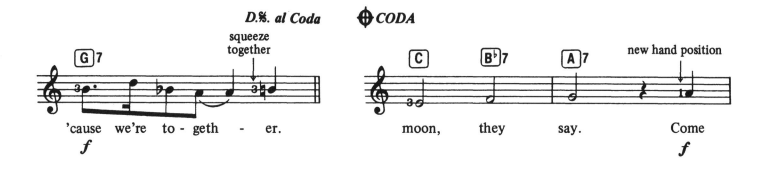

'cause we're to - geth - er. moon, they say. Come
f *f*

fly with me, _ let's fly, let's fly _ a - way. *ff*
stop rhythm

HOW DEEP IS YOUR LOVE

Words & Music by Barry Gibb, Robin Gibb & Maurice Gibb

Suggested registration: guitar
Rhythm: rock
Tempo: medium (♩ = 108)

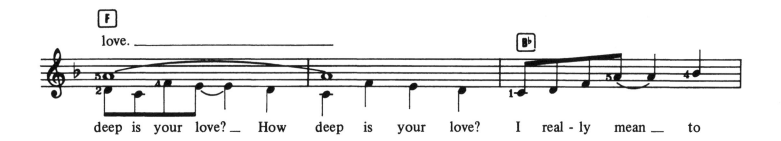

love. _____

deep is your love? How deep is your love? I real-ly mean __ to

cross over 5th finger

learn, __ 'cause we're liv-ing in a world of fools, break-ing us

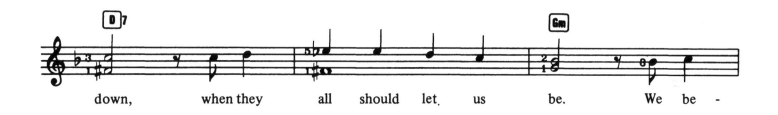

down, when they all should let us be. We be -

long to you and me.
mp

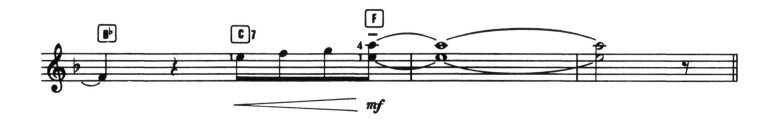

mf

ALWAYS ON MY MIND

Words & Music by Wayne Thompson, Mark James & Johnny Christopher

Suggested registration: synth
Rhythm: rock
Tempo: medium (♩ = 88)

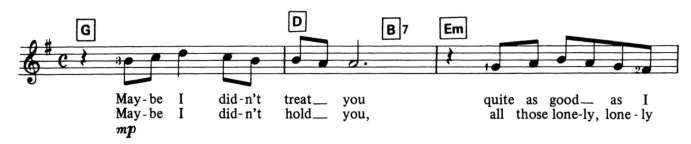

May-be I did-n't treat___ you quite as good___ as I
May-be I did-n't hold___ you, all those lone-ly, lone-ly

mp

should have.___ May - be I did - n't love___ you
times._____ And I guess I never told___ you

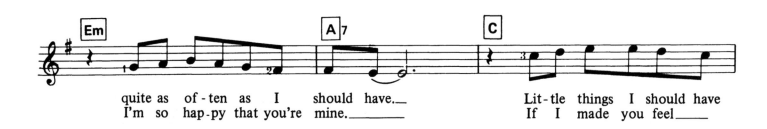

quite as of-ten as I should have.___ Lit-tle things I should have
I'm so hap-py that you're mine._____ If I made you feel___

said and done,___ I just nev - er took the time._____
sec - ond best,___ I'm so sor - ry, I was blind._____

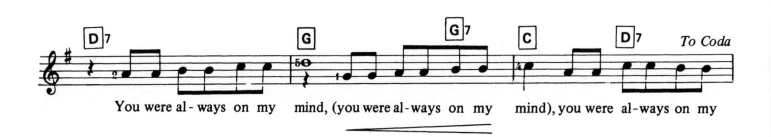

You were al-ways on my mind, (you were al-ways on my mind), you were al-ways on my

To Coda

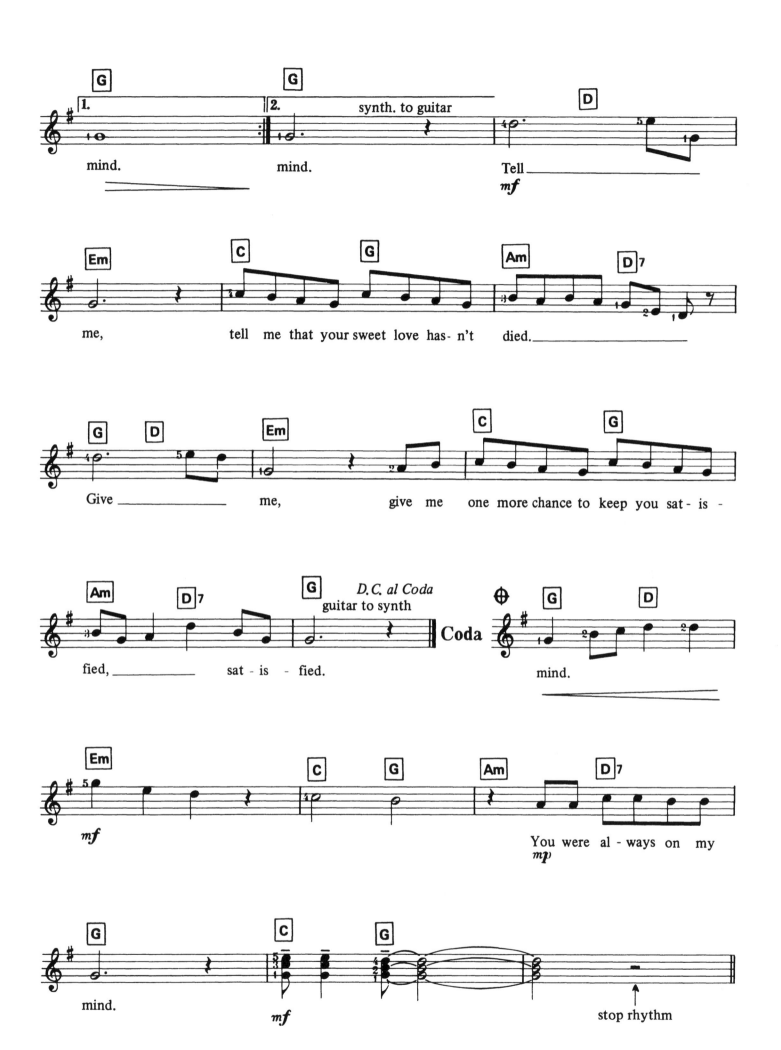

mind.

mind.

synth. to guitar

Tell _____

mf

me,

tell me that your sweet love has-n't died. _____

Give _____

me,

give me one more chance to keep you sat-is-

fied, _____

sat-is-fied.

D.C. al Coda
guitar to synth

Coda

mind.

You were al-ways on my
mp

mf

mind.

mf

stop rhythm

81

WORDS

Words & Music by Barry Gibb, Robin Gibb & Maurice Gibb

Suggested registration: piano
Rhythm: rock
Tempo: fairly slow (♩ = 84)

Smile an ev - er - last - ing smile, a smile could bring you near to me. _____
mp

_____ Don't ev - er let me find you gone, 'cause that would bring a

tear to me. _____ This world has lost its glo - ry,
mf

let's start a brand new sto - ry now, my love. _____ Right
mp

now, there'll be no oth - er time, and I can show you how, my

love. _____ Talk in ev - er - last -ing words, and ded - i - cate them

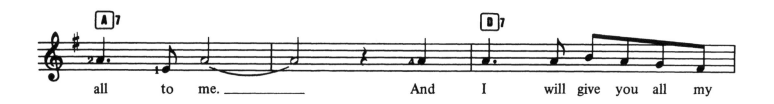

all to me. _____ And I will give you all my

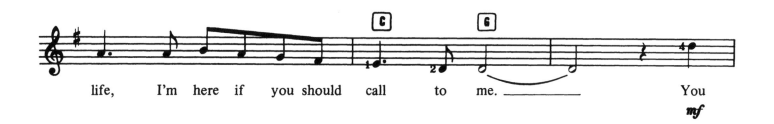

life, I'm here if you should call to me. _____ You

think that I don't ev - en mean a sin - gle word I say.

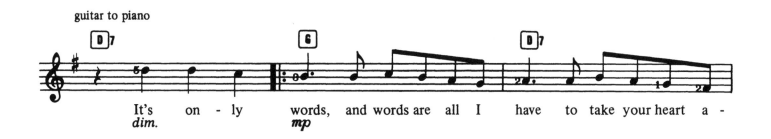

It's on - ly words, and words are all I have to take your heart a -

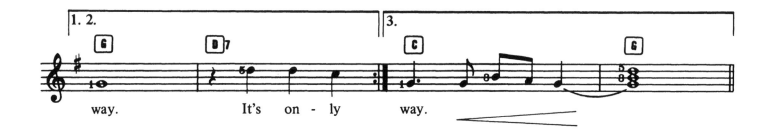

way. It's on - ly way.

LADY MADONNA

Words & Music by John Lennon & Paul McCartney

Suggested registration: harpsichord (with sustain)
Rhythm: rock
Tempo: medium (♩ = 104)

La - dy Ma - don - na, child - ren at your feet, won-der how you man - age to make ends meet.

Who finds the mon-ey, when you pay the rent, did you think that mon-ey was hea - ven sent?

Fri - day night ar - rives with-out a suit - case, Sun - day morn-ing creep in like a nun. Mon- day's child has learned to tie his

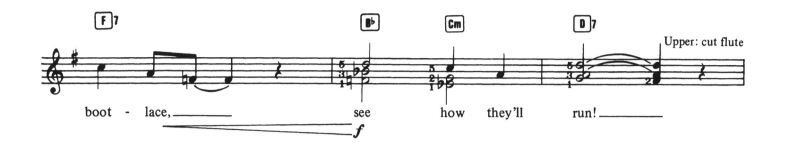

boot - lace,_____ see how they'll run!_____

f

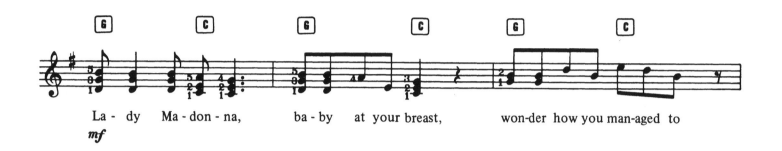

La - dy Ma - don - na, ba - by at your breast, won-der how you man-aged to

mf

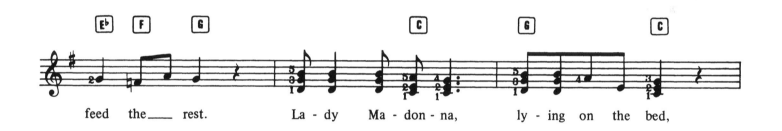

feed the___ rest. La - dy Ma - don - na, ly - ing on the bed,

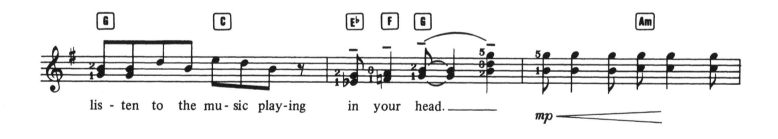

lis - ten to the mu - sic play-ing in your head._____

mp

mp _____ *mf*

stop rhythm

ROCKET MAN

Words & Music by Elton John & Bernie Taupin

Suggested registration: brass ensemble or brass synthesizer + arpeggio if available
Rhythm: 16 beat (or rock)
Tempo: slow (♩ = 66)

She packed my bags last night pre - flight,_ ze-ro hour,_ nine a. m._

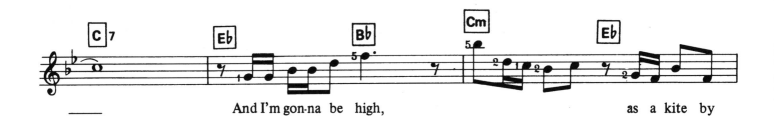

_ And I'm gon-na be high, as a kite by

then. I miss the earth so much, I

miss my wife,_ it's lone - ly out in space.

On such a time_____ less flight._

BABY, COME TO ME

Words & Music by Rod Temperton

Suggested registration: piano
Rhythm: rock
Tempo: medium (♩ = 88)

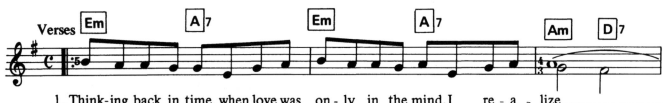

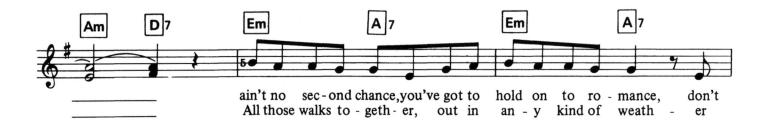

1. Think-ing back in time, when love was on-ly in the mind, I re-a-lize _____
2. Spend-in' ev-'ry dime to keep you talk-in' on the line, that's how it was. _____

mp

_____ ain't no sec-ond chance, you've got to hold on to ro-mance, don't
_____ All those walks to-geth-er, out in an-y kind of weath-er

let it slide. _____ There's a spe-cial kind of mag-ic in the
just be-cause. _____ There's a brand new way of look-ing at your

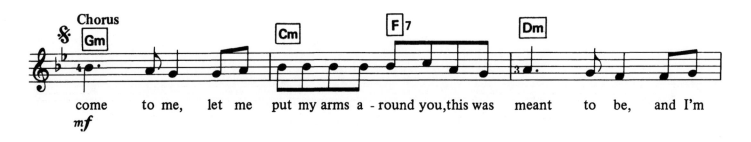

add strings

air, _____ when you find an-oth-er heart that needs to share. _____ Ba-by,
life, _____ when you know that love is stand-ing by your side. _____ Ba-by,

Chorus

come to me, let me put my arms a-round you, this was meant to be, and I'm

mf

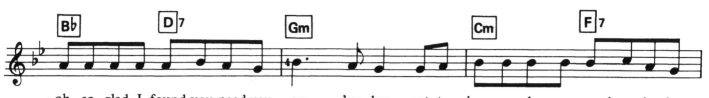

oh, so glad I found you, need you ev - 'ry day, got to have your love a - round me, ba - by,

al - ways stay, 'cause I can't go back to liv - in' with - out you.

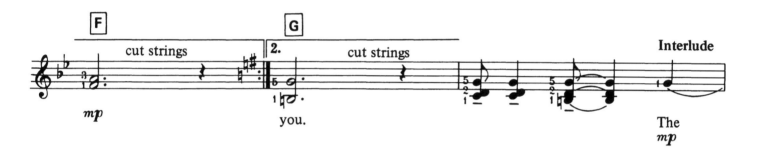

cut strings   2.   cut strings   Interlude

mp   you.   The   *mp*

night   can get   cold,   there's a   chill to   ev - 'ry   eve - ning

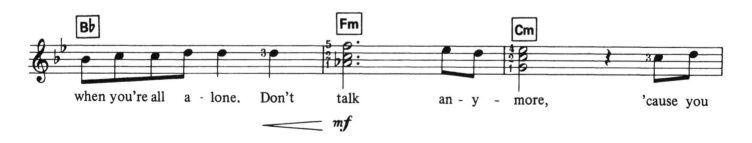

when you're all   a - lone.   Don't   talk   an - y - more,   'cause you

mf

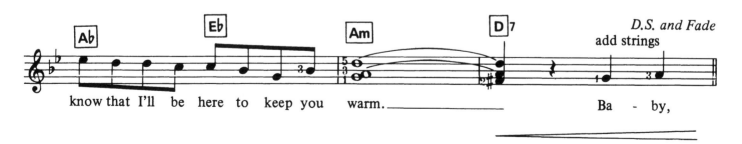

D.S. and Fade
add strings

know that I'll   be   here to   keep you   warm.   Ba - by,

IF YOU LEAVE ME NOW

Words & Music by Peter Cetera

Suggested registration: string ensemble
Rhythm: rock
Tempo: fairly slow (♩ = 88)
Synchro-start on

If you leave me now,— you'll take a - way the big - gest
leave me now,— you'll take a - way the ver - y

part of me.— Ooh,— no,— ba - by
heart of me.— Ooh,— no,— ba - by

please don't go.— And if you
please don't go.—

Ooh,— girl,— I just want you to stay.—

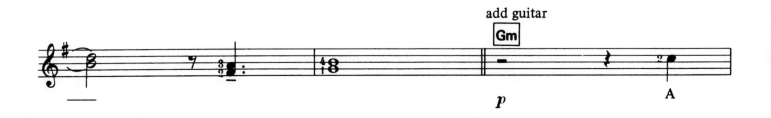

add guitar

love   like   ours is   love that's hard to   find._____

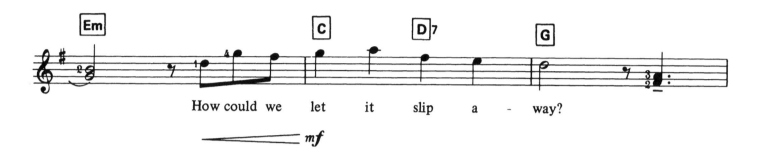

How could we   let it slip a - way?

mf

We've   come too far to

p

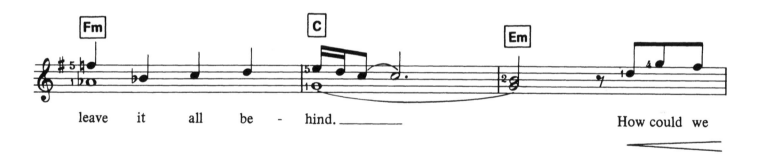

leave   it all be - hind._____   How could we

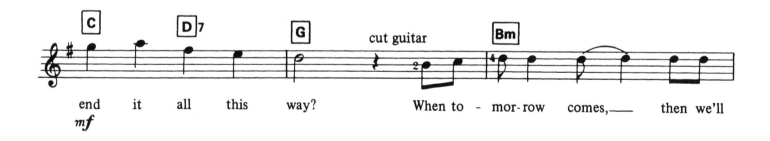

end   it all this   way?   When to - mor-row comes,___ then we'll

cut guitar

mf

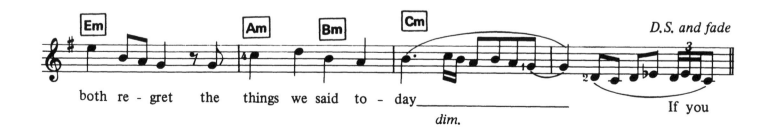

both re - gret   the things we said to - day_____   If you

dim.

D.S. and fade

ALL OR NOTHING AT ALL

Words & Music by Arthur Altman & Jack Lawrence

Suggested registration: string ensemble
Rhythm: beguine (or rhumba)
Tempo: quite fast ($\quarternote$ = 138)

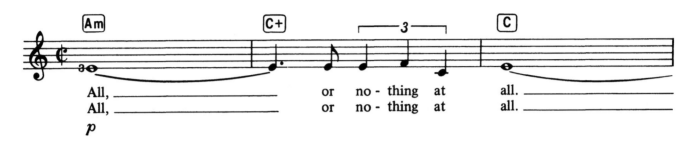

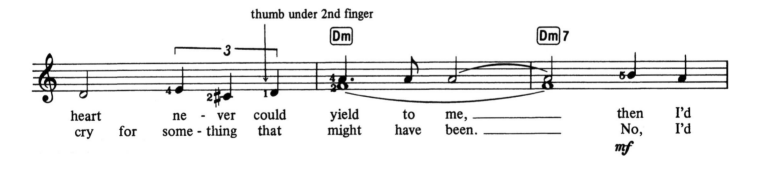

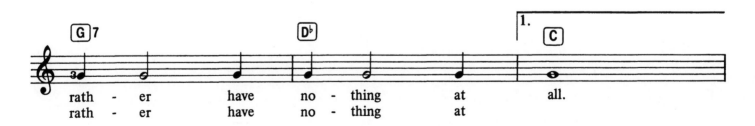

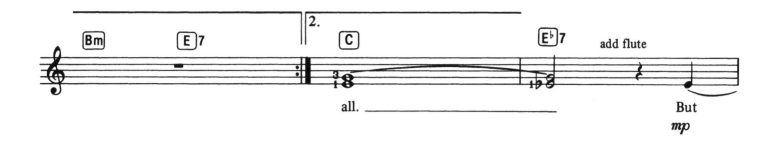

all. _____ But

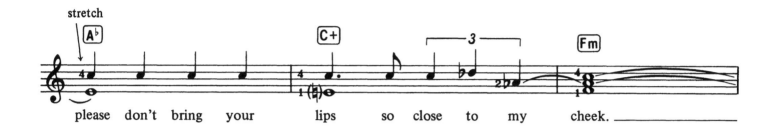

please don't bring your lips so close to my cheek. _____

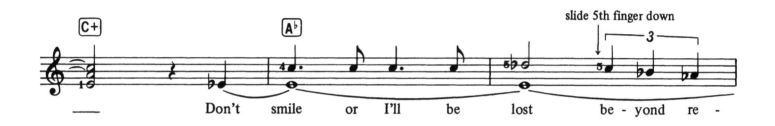

_____ Don't smile or I'll be lost be - yond re -

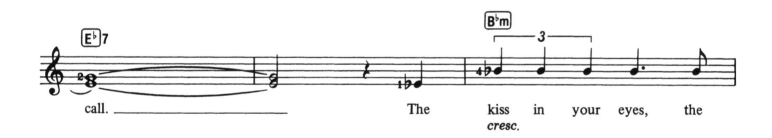

call. _____ The kiss in your eyes, the

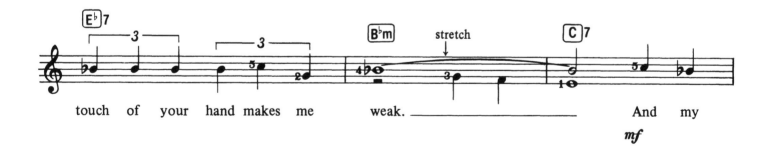

touch of your hand makes me weak. _____ And my

heart may grow diz - zy, and fall.

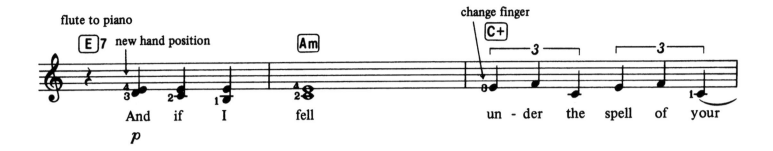

And if I fell

un - der the spell of your

call.

I would

be caught in the un - der - tow.

So you see, I've got to say: no!

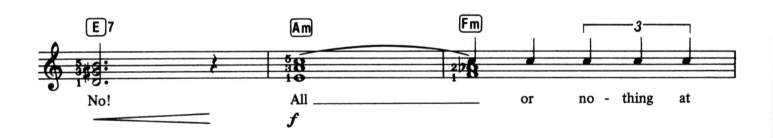

No! All or no - thing at

all.

MASTER CHORD CHART

C
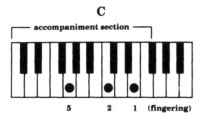
5   2   1 (fingering)

Cm
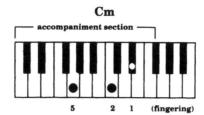
5   2   1 (fingering)

C7
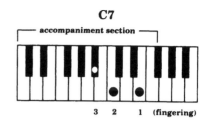
3   2   1 (fingering)

D♭
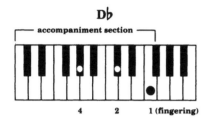
4   2   1 (fingering)

C♯m
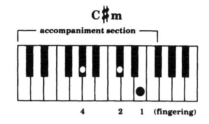
4   2   1 (fingering)

D♭(C♯)7
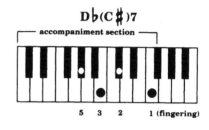
5   3   2   1 (fingering)

D
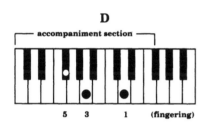
5   3   1   (fingering)

Dm
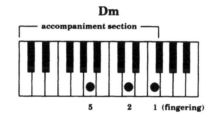
5   2   1 (fingering)

D7
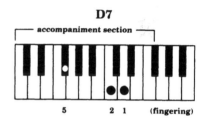
5   2   1   (fingering)

E♭
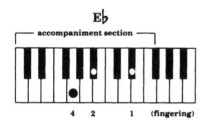
4   2   1 (fingering)

E♭m
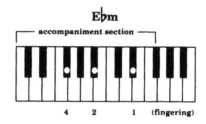
4   2   1 (fingering)

E♭7
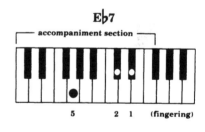
5   2   1   (fingering)

E
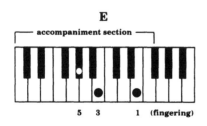
5   3   1 (fingering)

Em
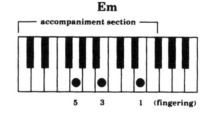
5   3   1 (fingering)

E7
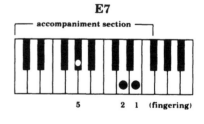
5   2   1   (fingering)

F
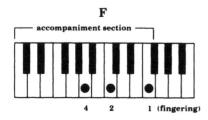
4   2   1 (fingering)

Fm
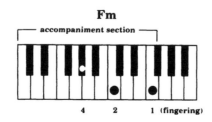
4   2   1 (fingering)

F7
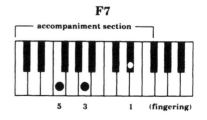
5   3   1 (fingering)

MASTER CHORD CHART

G♭(F♯)

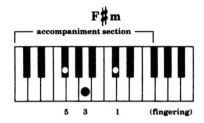

F♯m

G♭(F♯)7

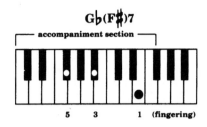

G

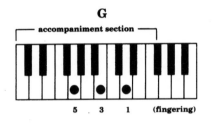

Gm

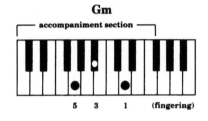

G7

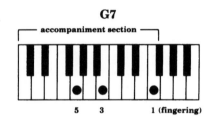

A♭

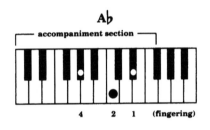

A♭m

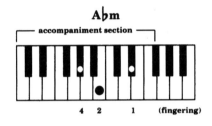

A♭7

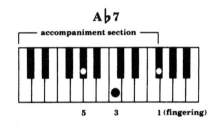

A

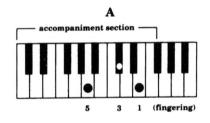

Am

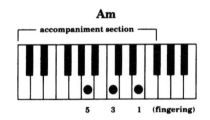

A7

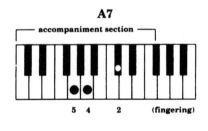

B♭

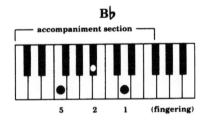

B♭m

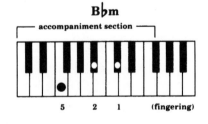

B♭7

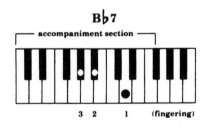

B

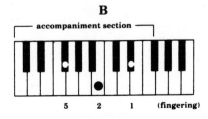

Bm

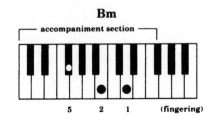

B7

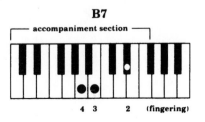